Developing Reading Comprehension Skills Years 5–6

Classic Poetry

Kate Heap

Publisher's information

We hope you and your pupils enjoy using the ideas in this book. Brilliant Publications publishes many other books to help primary school teachers. To find out more details on all of our titles, including those listed below, please go to our website: www.brilliantpublications.co.uk.

Books in the Developing Reading Comprehension Skills series:
- Classic Poetry Years 3-4
- Classic Poetry Years 5-6
- Classic Children's Literature Years 3-4
- Classic Children's Literature Years 5-6
- Contemporary Children's Literature Years 3-4
- Contemporary Children's Literature Years 5-6
- Non-fiction Years 3-4
- Non-fiction Years 5-6

Brilliant Activities for Reading Comprehension series
Getting to Grips with English Grammar series
Brilliant Activities for Creative Writing series
Brilliant Activities for Grammar and Punctuation series
Boost Creative Writing series

Published by Brilliant Publications Limited
Unit 10
Sparrow Hall Farm
Edlesborough
Dunstable
Bedfordshire
LU6 2ES, UK

www.brilliantpublications.co.uk

Written by Kate Heap

Printed ISBN: 978-0-85747-846-7
ePDF ISBN: 978-0-85747-847-4
First printed in 2021

Dedication

To Mum, Dad & Jane
Thank you for introducing me to the magic of words
and for being my very first cheerleaders.

About the Author

Kate Heap

Kate has always loved books, her childhood overflowing with the adventures found within their pages. Now, as both a teacher and a parent, one of her greatest joys and privileges is sharing her love of literature with children.

Born and raised in Canada, Kate began her teaching career with Regina Public Schools. Ready for new adventures, she moved to the UK in 2001. Kate has spent many rewarding years in Leeds schools guiding children through the world of learning. She has supported primary school teachers through her roles of Literacy Leader, Leading Literacy Teacher for Leeds, Advanced Skills Teacher and Senior Leadership with responsibility for Assessment.

As a Primary English Consultant, Kate is now able to share her knowledge and enthusiasm even further. She enjoys reviewing children's literature for her blog, Scope for Imagination, working with authors and publishers to spread the word about their incredible books, and is passionate about helping teachers, parents and children find just the right ones for them. In her series, *Developing Reading Comprehension Skills*, Kate has created classroom resources that support both children and teachers in their quest to achieve key objectives and prepare for assessment while fostering a love of literature.

Kate is adventuring through life with her ever supportive husband, three wonderful children and two very special cats.

Contents

Introduction

> ***Classic:*** Judged over a period of time to be of the highest quality and outstanding of its kind; a work of art of recognised and established value. (Oxford English Dictionary)

Why Classic Poems?

Classic poems are those which have stood the test of time. Their meaning is universal and timeless: as true now as it was when it was first written. Their language causes the reader to think and to feel. These poems take readers beyond their own circumstances and change how they see the world. Classic poems give the reader a window into the past, to another time or another place, while building empathy and understanding. These poems become a part of our shared language and tradition. When children learn these poems, they gain access to a common cultural language and an understanding of so many literary references.

The world of classic poetry is a place to escape. With the power to transform and change the way readers see the world, poetry can provide peace, inspiration, hope and focus. It opens up a world where playing with language is the norm and there is no one right answer. Children enjoy poetry for so many different reasons. They are able to explore language while gaining an awareness of words and their meaning. The musicality of poetry builds a sense of rhythm while developing emotional intelligence. Poems may be silly, funny or scary. They might address death, loss, remembrance, hope, love or joy. So much is expressed in so few words making them much more accessible than full novels. When reading a poem, children bring their own thoughts, experiences and emotions to the meaning making them intensely personal. Giving children the opportunity to learn these poems gives them the opportunity to find out more about themselves and the world around them.

In recent years, we have seen a number of changes to the Key Stage 2 English Curriculum, the Key Stage 2 Reading Test Framework and in the overall expectations for pupils. A focus on higher level vocabulary and increased use of more classic style texts and language has presented new challenges for both teachers and children. There is an expectation that children will have a strong understanding of a wide range of language devices. Poetry is the perfect avenue for exploring them.

By the end of Year 6, children are expected to have many skills linked to poetry. These objectives from the National Curriculum outline just some of the links to poetry:

Pupils should be taught to maintain positive attitudes to reading and understanding of what they read by:

- continuing to read and discuss an increasingly wide range of fiction, poetry, plays, non-fiction and reference books or textbooks
- identifying and discussing themes and conventions in and across a wide range of writing
- learning a wider range of poetry by heart

- preparing poems and plays to read aloud and to perform, showing understanding through intonation, tone and volume so that the meaning is clear to an audience.

It is essential that children become familiar with the wealth of classic poetry from both Great Britain and other countries. The richness of language and universality of themes provided by these types of texts allow children to expand their understanding of the world. They are then better able to make links between literature, history, geography, science and other areas.

In this book, children in Years 5–6 are exposed to a range of these rich poems. It is just a small sample of the thousands of wonderful poems that teachers and children may wish to read and study. Through these poems, children are given opportunities to tackle more complex vocabulary and widen their knowledge of synonyms, develop understanding of challenging language devices and practise each of the eight Reading Content Domain question types. It is also my hope that children will want to read more poetry and have the opportunity to discover some of the greatest poems ever written.

The poems selected for this book have been intentionally chosen to provide teachers with a variety of poets, topics and themes. This broadens the range of children's reading and ensures there will something of interest for every reader.

Female Poets: UK
Elizabeth Barrett Browning: A Musical Instrument (1860)
Christina Rossetti: In the Bleak Midwinter (1872)
Female Poets: International
Emily Dickinson: "Hope" is the Thing with Feathers (1891), USA
Lucy Maud Montgomery: An Autumn Evening (1916), Canada
Amy Lowell: Night Clouds (1925), USA
Rachel Field: North of Time (1936), USA
Male Poets: UK
William Blake: The Tyger (1794)
Alfred Noyes: The Highwayman (1906)
W.H. Davies: Leisure (1911), Wales
Walter de la Mare: The Listeners (1912)
Male Poets: International
Rudyard Kipling: The Way Through the Woods (1910), UK/India
John McCrae: In Flanders Fields (1915), Canada

Publication Date	**Poem Title & Author**	**Theme**
1794	The Tyger by *William Blake*	Good vs Evil / Nature
1860	A Musical Instrument by *Elizabeth Barrett Browning*	Destruction of Nature / Gods
1872	In the Bleak Midwinter by *Christina Rossetti*	Christmas / Nativity
1891	"Hope" is the Thing with Feathers by *Emily Dickinson*	Hope Enduring
1906	The Highwayman by *Alfred Noyes*	Love / Death
1910	The Way Through the Woods by *Rudyard Kipling*	Nature / Human Impact
1911	Leisure by W.H. Davies	Life / Priorities
1912	The Listeners by *Walter de la Mare*	Silence / Unanswered Questions
1915	In Flanders Fields by *John McCrae*	War / Hope
1916	An Autumn Evening by *Lucy Maud Montgomery*	Nature / Beauty
1925	Night Clouds by *Amy Lowell*	Nature / Beauty
1936	North of Time by *Rachel Field*	Death / Life as a Journey

How to use this book

Reading, understanding, writing and performing poetry should be a key part of any school's English curriculum. Exposure to this wonderful style of writing is so important and must not be just an add-on. Key poems must be carefully selected and built into a broad plan for English so children do not miss out on these wonderful experiences. The poems and questions in this book can be easily used as the skeleton for some of these poetry units and then be built up with further activities in the classroom.

The poems in this book are ordered from easier to more difficult. Teachers may wish to use them in this order, select poems linked to class topics/themes or choose those they think will most interest the class.

The content domain question types are organised in the order in which they appear in the English Reading Test Framework for National Curriculum tests, but it is important that teachers think about the needs of their class and choose content domains accordingly. Teachers may wish to begin with more basic retrieval before moving on to more difficult content domains such as vocabulary or author's use of language. You will notice there are more vocabulary, retrieval, inference and author's use of language questions than the other content domains. This reflects the weighting of the question types in the KS2 Reading SATs papers, the nature of the poems and gives children more opportunities to practise these skills.

The poems and questions have been designed to work well within a variety of teaching styles: whole class sessions, smaller teacher-led sessions or child-led groups. They may be used as a supported or independent task. The flexibility of this resource means it can be used in many different ways.

Each unit, consisting of a poem and eight question types, should be taught over a number of sessions, allowing the teacher time to really focus on the strategies needed to answer each question type. These units should be used as taught lessons rather than as assessment tools as there is so much scope for discussion to deepen children's understanding of the language and themes. No matter how the units are used, children should always finish with reading through the poem again so they can apply everything they have learned and gain a deeper understanding of the meaning as a whole.

Some of the poems are intentionally difficult (much like the KS2 Reading SATs papers). However, the accompanying questions have been designed to guide children through the texts and help them to develop their comprehension and reading skills. All of the extracts have been trialled by Key Stage 2 children. They found that, at first, the poems seemed quite difficult, but once they worked through the questions they understood what the poems were about, had learned a lot of new vocabulary and gained insights into the meaning.

Poetry Toolkit

Before children begin to read these poems, it is important that they have an understanding of their "Poetry Toolkit". This is the collection of poetic (language) devices used in poems to create images and meaning. I like to encourage children to keep these "tools" with them whenever they read poetry so they are ready to make connections and build their understanding. You may wish to display these tools in the classroom or even create a toolbox with real or play tools labelled with each poetic device.

Tool	Meaning
Imagery	The creation of mental images through description.
Simile	Comparing one thing to another by saying it is "like" or "as" that other thing
Metaphor	Something that represents or is a symbol of something else. The characteristics of one thing are similar to the characteristics of another
Personification	Giving a human characteristic to an inanimate object, animal or abstract concept
Alliteration	Repetition of the same initial sound in closely located words
Assonance	Repetition of the same vowel sound in the middle of closely located words
Consonance	Repetition of the same consonant sound in the middle of closely located words
Repetition	Repeating the same word or phrase for effect
Onomatopoeia	A word that imitates the sound it is describing (eg, pop)
Rhythm	The pattern or beat created by the syllables and stressed sounds in a line of poetry
Rhyme	Repetition of the ending sounds of words (often at the end of lines of poetry)

Using Poems in the Classroom

The richness of these poems provides endless classroom opportunities. Rather than just reading and analysing the stand-alone poems, teachers and their students may wish to bring them to life through further exploration together. Take advantage of the seasons and special days to read appropriate poems: autumn, spring, Remembrance Day, Christmas ... , there are so many links to be made with poetry. Poems learned around days that are special to children are likely to be remembered and recalled when these special occasions come around again in the future.

Children may be inspired to write in a similar style or use the content of the poem to inspire their own compositions across a range of genres and purposes. The best writing often comes from meaningful classroom activities based on high-quality texts.

The classic poems in this book lend themselves to a whole host of teaching activities. I would encourage teachers to use these texts as a springboard to jump off into further learning.

- Speaking and listening activities such as expressing opinions, questioning, description, persuasion and debate
- Learn poems by heart and for performance
- Drama activities such as role play, hot seating, freeze-frame and characterisation (My Year 6 classes have thoroughly enjoyed hot seating the characters from The Highwayman with props and then holding a court case to debate who is to blame for Bess' death.)
- Explore different styles of poetry. Which do the children prefer: narrative, sonnet, haiku, rhyme or no rhyme?
- Examine how poetry "breaks the rules" of punctuation and grammar
- Compare perspectives on the same topic. Look at contrasting poems by the same or different authors. Does everyone see things the same way? This could be a simple comparison of descriptions of nature or a more complex analysis of opinions about the First World War (look at John McCrae, Wilfred Owen and Rupert Brooke)
- Historical research into the author, time period, technology, links to historical events, comparisons between time periods or a related educational visit
- Biographies of authors or historical characters
- Geographical research into the setting location, study of geographical features (eg, islands, mountains, seas) and map drawing
- ICT links such as computer animation, short films, reviews, advertisements and recording their own poems complete with sound effects
- Explore how painting, drawing or sculpture might represent the poem
- Use physical movement (dance or gymnastics) to interpret the meaning
- Poem to video comparisons (There are many animated versions of classic poems)
- Read a "Poem a Day" to expose children to a wide range of poems – both classic and more contemporary

- Watch poetry videos: Michael Rosen, Shel Silverstein and The Poetry Foundation website are just a few examples of fantastic videos available.

Follow the children's lead. With some poems, they will be happy to read, practise the question types and move on while other poems will capture their imaginations and natural curiosity. Grab this and run with it! They may be whisked away into the mystery of The Listeners or enchanted by the setting of Night Clouds. They might be intrigued by The Tyger or struck by the meaning of Leisure. Take time to explore and develop their curiosity. It will inspire a life-long love of poetry.

Reading Content Domain

Vocabulary

Give or explain the meaning of words in context.

The ***Vocabulary*** content domain is not only about the words children know but also the strategies they possess for working out the meaning of words they don't know. Children must use the context of the surrounding line, stanza or entire poem to work out the meaning of the words. By thinking about what has been happening in the poem so far and searching for clues, children are able to learn new words and expand their vocabulary. This content domain draws heavily on children's understanding of synonyms and their ability to use the "replacement method" in which they remove the word in question and replace it with each option in turn to find the best fit.

Example: ***The Listeners***

In the question below, replace "*perplexed*" with each option to find the best fit answer.

"*Where he stood perplexed and still.*"

Which word is closest in meaning to perplexed?

	Tick **one**
quiet	
confused	
frightened	
alone	

Retrieval

Retrieve and record information / identify key details from fiction and non-fiction.

The ***Retrieval*** content domain is about children being able to find key pieces of information in the poem. Using keywords and a highlighting strategy will help children to make links between the keywords in the question and similar wording in the poem. By scanning the poem, they can spot the keywords, highlight them and find their answer. It is important to note that it may not be the exact wording from the question in the poem. Synonyms may be used.

Example: ***The Tyger***

In the question below, the keywords are **tools** and **brain**. Once children find these words (or synonyms for them) in the poem, they will be able to find their answer.

Name four tools used to create the Tyger's brain.

Summary

Summarise main ideas from more than one paragraph.

The ***Summary*** content domain is about children being able to sum up or condense what they have read. This may involve identifying the key points of the poem or coming up with an appropriate heading for a stanza. In these questions, more than one answer may be correct, but children must choose what they believe to be the best or most appropriate answer and then justify their choice. Discussion about the different options is key to help children understand that many poems have more than one theme.

Example: ***An Autumn Evening***

In the question below, children are asked to identify the main idea/lesson of the entire poem. They need to choose the answer that provides the best overall meaning.

What is the **main message** of this poem?

	Tick **one**
Sunsets are beautiful	
Winter is just around the corner	
Stop and take in the beauty of nature	
Life is fleeting and passes quickly	

Inference

Make inferences from the text / explain and justify inferences with evidence from the text.

The ***Inference*** content domain is about children being detectives and looking for clues in the poem to support their answers. It is important for them to remember that whenever they make a point (or give an answer), they also need to provide a quote from or reference to the poem that proves what they are saying.

Example: ***The Highwayman***

In the question below, children will find that the character of Tim is weak, sneaky and dirty (among other things). For each characteristic they identify, they must make a direct reference to the text to prove it.

Read the verse beginning: "*And dark in the dark old inn-yard a stable-wicket creaked...*" What impression is given of Tim's character? **Use evidence** from the poem to support your answer.

Prediction

Predict what might happen from details stated and implied.

The ***Prediction*** content domain is about making logical or reasonable predictions about what might happen later in the poem. Children should be able to back up their ideas with evidence from the poem that has led them to believe in their predictions.

> Example: ***North of Time***
>
> In the question below, children need to put themselves in the place of the narrator and decide what they think she might do in the future. They must be able to justify their predictions by referring to the impact of what the old man said in the poem.
>
> After listening to the old man's stories of his life and his grandfather, how do you think the narrator will choose to live her life?
>
> **Use evidence** from the poem to support your prediction.

Text Meaning

Identify/explain how information/narrative content is related and contributes to meaning as a whole.

The ***Text Meaning*** content domain is about identifying the structural and language features of the poem and understanding the role of each part of the poem. This includes explaining how certain parts of a poem help to create or change the overall meaning.

Example: ***North of Time***
In the question below, children are required to match each feature of the poem with an example.

Draw lines to match each poetic technique with the correct quotation from the poem.

alliteration	Folks nowadays are like as peas in a pod,
onomatopoeia	The clocks ticks told
personification	I could hear the boom of the turning tide along the island shore.
simile	We sat together in the small, square room,

In poetry, there will also be questions about the rhyme scheme and rhythm of the poem. Children may be asked to identify the pattern of the rhyme. Each new sound at the end of a line is assigned a different letter. The rhyme scheme might be in couplets (AABB) or alternate rhyme (ABAB).
The rhythm of the poem is the beat or syllables in each line. Children will need to consider the number of syllables, line length and how these affect how the poem sounds.

Example: "***Hope" is the Thing with Feathers***
What is the rhyme scheme of this poem? Verse one has been done for you.

Verse one: ABCB

Verse two: ________________

Verse three: ________________

Apart from the first line, there is a consistent rhythm to this poem. The number of syllables in each line follows a pattern.

a) What is the pattern?

____

b) What impact does this rhythm have on how the poem sounds?

____

Author's Use of Language

Identify/explain how meaning is enhanced through choice of words and phrases.

The ***Author's Use of Language*** content domain is about children recognising figurative language and descriptive phrases that contribute to the overall meaning of the poem. Once children spot these features, they need to both understand what the features mean and identify the impact on the reader. There are various strategies children may use to answer these types of questions.

a) Mind Map method – Children identify the keyword in the question and place it at the centre of a mind map (spider diagram). They then write down everything they know about the word. Once they have thought through all of the possible meanings or associations of the word, they choose the most logical or best fit ideas to create their answer. If there is more than one word identified in the question, children should make sure they include an explanation or reference to each word in their answer.

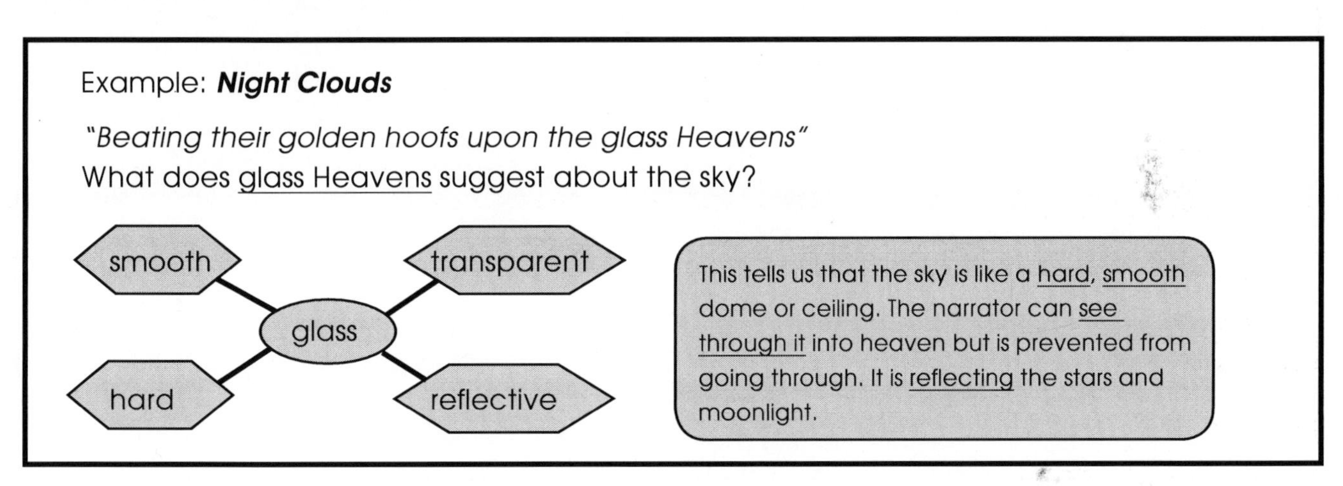
Example: Night Clouds
"Beating their golden hoofs upon the glass Heavens"
What does glass Heavens suggest about the sky?
smooth
transparent
glass
hard
reflective
This tells us that the sky is like a hard, smooth dome or ceiling. The narrator can see through it into heaven but is prevented from going through. It is reflecting the stars and moonlight.

b) Replacement method as described in the Vocabulary content domain.

c) Identify figurative language techniques (simile, metaphor, imagery, personification etc.) and write about how the author is using that technique.

Example: **The Highwayman**

In the question below, the metaphor of hell helps the reader to identify the type of thing (or person) that might stop the Highwayman from returning to Bess.

"I'll come to thee by moonlight, though hell should bar the way."

The poet is using a metaphor in this line. What might stop the Highwayman from returning to Bess?

Compare and Contrast

Make comparisons within the text.

The ***Comparison*** content domain is about children identifying how characters, settings, events or moods in a poem are similar or different to each other. It also requires children to identify how a character changes over the course of a poem. When answering these questions, children must choose the most appropriate conjunction to link their ideas together as they build their answer.

To Show Similarity / Compare	To Show Difference / Contrast
similarly	but
also	however
in addition	on the other hand
in the same way	whereas
they are both...	while
likewise	yet
equally	unlike

Example: ***In the Bleak Midwinter***

In the question below, children are asked to identify how the narrator is different from the other characters in the Nativity in her gift giving. The use of contrasting conjunctions makes the answer very clear.

How is the narrator different from the shepherd and Wise Man?

The shepherd and Wise Man bring physical gifts to the baby while/but/however the narrator gives her love (an abstract noun).

Night Clouds

by Amy Lowell

The white mares of the moon rush along the sky
Beating their golden hoofs upon the glass Heavens;
The white mares of the moon are all standing on their hind legs
Pawing at the green porcelain doors of the remote Heavens
Fly, mares!
Strain your utmost
Scatter the milky dust of stars,
Or the tiger sun will leap upon you and destroy you
With one lick of his vermillion tongue

Vocabulary

Night Clouds

1. **Find** and **copy one word** that is closest in meaning to pottery.

____

2. *"The white mares of the moon rush along the sky"*

Which word is closest in meaning to mares?

	Tick **one**
clouds	
lights	
horses	
stars	

3. *"Beating their golden hoofs upon the glass Heavens"*

What does Beating their golden hoofs mean in this line?

____

4. **Find** and **copy one word** that tell you the Heavens are far away.

____

5. What is the poet telling the horses when she says, *"Strain your utmost"*?

	Tick **one**
Go higher!	
Run faster!	
Don't give up!	
Try your hardest!	

6. **Find** and **copy one word** that tells you the colour of the tiger's tongue.

____

Retrieval

Night Clouds

1. **Find** and **copy the four** actions of the white mares.

1. ______________________________

2. ______________________________

3. ______________________________

4. ______________________________

2. What time of day is it in the first half of the poem?

	Tick **one**
dawn	
night	
sunset	
morning	

3. What does the poet think will happen as the mares fly away?

____

4. How will the tiger destroy the mares?

____

5. Using information from the text, put a tick in the correct box to show whether each statement is **true** or **false**.

	True	**False**
The sky is filled with stars.		
The door to the Heavens is open.		
The poet thinks it will be easy for the mares to escape.		
The tiger will destroy them with his paw.		

Summary Night Clouds

1. Why is the title so important in this poem?

	Tick **one**
It tells the reader it is at night.	
It is the only mention of clouds.	
It tells the reader there are animals in the poem.	

2. One of the big ideas in this poem is the sky as a living, breathing animal that is always changing. Do you agree with this? Explain with reference to the poem.

____

____

____

____

____

____

Inference Night Clouds

1. The two animals in this poem are an **analogy** (an extended comparison) for the sky.
What part of the sky does each animal represent?

Animal	Represents
mares	
tiger	

2. What **evidence** is there that the mares are anxious as they run across the sky?

____

____

3. *"Pawing at the green porcelain doors of the remote Heavens"*
Why do the mares do this?

	Tick **one**
The door is locked.	
They are trying to find something.	
They are trying to get away from the tiger.	
Their owner has called them.	

Night Clouds

4. **Which word** best describes the character of the tiger in this poem?

	Tick **one**
bold	
timid	
kind	
fierce	

5. According to the poem, how do we know it won't be difficult for the tiger to destroy the mares?

____

6. Based on what you have read in the poem, which animal does the poet prefer? Make reference to the poem in your answer.

____

____

____

____

____

____

Prediction Night Clouds

1. What will happen when the sun rises?
Use evidence from the poem to support your prediction.

Text Meaning Night Clouds

1. Draw lines to match each poetic technique with the correct quotation from the poem.

alliteration	the green porcelain doors
personification	rush along the sky
alliteration	The white mares of the moon
description	Beating their golden hoofs upon the glass Heavens

2. What is the impact of the three shorter lines in the middle of the poem?

___

___

___

Author's Use of Language

Night Clouds

1. a) The poet portrays the mares, the clouds and the night as good.
Find and **copy two words or phrases** she uses to do this.

1. ______________________________

2. ______________________________

1. b) The tiger and the sunrise are portrayed as bad.
Find and **copy two words or phrases** that show this.

1. ______________________________

2. ______________________________

2. The poet uses a lot of description in this poem. Which sense does she appeal to the most?

Circle one

	taste	touch
hearing	sight	smell

3. *"Beating their golden hoofs upon the glass Heavens"*
What does glass Heavens suggest about the sky?

____

4. *"Scatter the milky dust of stars"*
What impression does this line give the reader of the night sky?

____

5. How does the poet show the change from night to morning in this poem?

____

Compare and Contrast — Night Clouds

1. a) Give **one** way the mares and the tiger are similar.

____

b) Give **two** ways the mares and the tiger are different.

1. ____

2. ____

2. Why is the description of the mares a good analogy (extended comparison) for the night sky?

____

____

3. The poem has two clear sections. **Which word** in line 8 signals the change?

____

4. How is the description of the night different from the description of the day?

____

____

____

____

An Autumn Evening

by Lucy Maud Montgomery

Dark hills against a hollow crocus sky
Scarfed with its crimson pennons, and below
The dome of sunset long, hushed valleys lie
Cradling the twilight, where the lone winds blow
And wake among the harps of leafless trees
Fantastic runes and mournful melodies.

The chilly purple air is threaded through
With silver from the rising moon afar,
And from a gulf of clear, unfathomed blue
In the southwest glimmers a great gold star
Above the darkening druid glens of fir
Where beckoning boughs and elfin voices stir.

And so I wander through the shadows still,
And look and listen with a rapt delight,
Pausing again and yet again at will
To drink the elusive beauty of the night,
Until my soul is filled, as some deep cup,
That with divine enchantment is brimmed up.

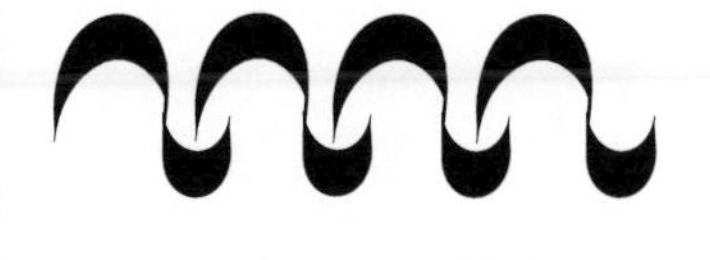

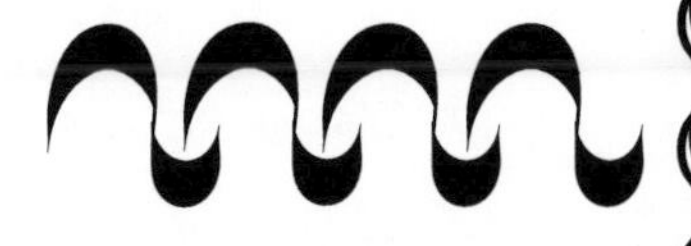

Vocabulary An Autumn Evening

1. Look at verse one.
Circle the word that is closest in meaning to flag.

crocus	pennons	dome	harps

2. "*...and below the dome of sunset...*"
What does the word dome mean and what does it suggest about the scene?

___

___

3. What is meant by the phrase "*Cradling the twilight*"?

___

4. Look at the line "*Fantastic runes and mournful melodies.*"
Explain the meaning of the words runes and mournful.

Word	Meaning
runes	
mournful	

5. "*And from a gulf of clear, unfathomed blue*"
What does this description suggest about the sky?

___

___

Retrieval

An Autumn Evening

1. **Find** and **copy five** colour words in this poem.

1. ______________________ 2. ______________________

3. ______________________ 4. ______________________

5. ______________________

2. The poet describes **four aspects of nature** in the poem. The first one has been named for you. What are the other **three**?

hills	

3. Which **three** things awaken at night?

1. ______________________

2. ______________________

3. ______________________

4. In the third verse, the action begins. **Find** and **copy the five** actions the narrator does.

1. ______________________

2. ______________________

3. ______________________

4. ______________________

5. ______________________

5. What happens to the narrator's soul at the end of the poem?

____

Summary An Autumn Evening

1. What is the main message of this poem?

	Tick **one**
Sunsets are beautiful	
Winter is just around the corner	
Stop and take in the beauty of nature	
Life is fleeting and passes quickly	

2. **Rewrite** the **final four lines** of the poem in your own words.

What is the narrator doing and why?

"Pausing again and yet again at will
To drink the elusive beauty of the night,
Until my soul is filled, as some deep cup,
There with divine enchantment is brimmed up."

___

___

___

___

___

Inference An Autumn Evening

1. In the first verse, the author creates a sense of quiet. **Find** and **copy two words or phrases** that help to create this.

2. Which **two words** show the value of the moon and stars?

3. **Find** and **copy a phrase** that gives the impression the narrator may not be alone.

4. *"And look and listen with a rapt delight"*
What does this line tell us about how the narrator feels in the third verse?

5. In the third verse, why does the narrator keep pausing?

Prediction

An Autumn Evening

1. Why must the narrator make the most of the autumn evening now? What is on its way? How will things change?

Make sure you refer to the poem in your answer.

2. If this poem was entitled *"Spring Evening"* with the same third verse, what things would be described in the first two verses? Use as many adjectives as you can in your suggestions.

Text Meaning An Autumn Evening

1. What is the rhyme scheme of this poem?

	Tick **one**
AAABBB	
ABABAB	
ABCABC	
ABABCC	

2. Write words from the poem to complete the pairs of rhyming words.

sky	
trees	
fir	
delight	

3. Draw lines to match each part of the poem with the correct quotation from the poem.

action	Scarfed with its crimson pennons
personification	Above the darkening druid
setting	And so I wander through the shadows
alliteration	Dark hills against a hollow crocus sky

Author's Use of Language

An Autumn Evening

1. In the first verse, the poet creates a sense of music.
Find and **copy two words or phrases** that suggest this.

---

2. *"The chilly purple air is threaded through*
With silver from the rising moon afar"
What does threaded through with silver suggest about the sky?

---

3. *"In the southwest glimmers a great gold star"*
What two impressions does this line give of the star?

---

4. There is a magical, mystical, pagan feel to this poem. **Find** and **copy four examples** of this.
1. ____________
2. ____________
3. ____________
4. ____________

5. In this poem, the poet uses some poetic devices. In the second verse, **find** and **copy a phrase** that is both **alliteration** and **personification**.

---

6. *"That with divine enchantment is brimmed up"*
What does the poet mean by **divine enchantment**?

Compare and Contrast

An Autumn Evening

1. In the first verse, the poet compares the hills to the sky. How are they different?

____

____

2. In verse two, how are the druid glens different at night compared to the daytime?

____

____

3. How do verses one and two differ from verse three?

____

____

In Flanders Fields

by John McCrae

In Flanders fields the poppies blow
Between the crosses, row on row,
That mark our place; and in the sky
The larks, still bravely singing, fly
Scarce heard amid the guns below.

We are the Dead. Short days ago
We lived, felt dawn, saw sunset glow,
Loved and were loved, and now we lie,
In Flanders fields.

Take up our quarrel with the foe:
To you from failing hands we throw
The torch; be yours to hold it high.
If ye break faith with us who die
We shall not sleep, though poppies grow
In Flanders fields.

Vocabulary In Flanders Fields

1. What is a lark?

___

2. Look at verse one.
Find and **copy one word** that is closest in meaning to <u>hardly</u>.

___

3. *"Take up our quarrel with the foe:"*
Which word is closest in meaning to <u>quarrel</u> in this line?

	Tick **one**
meeting	
fight	
argument	
complaint	

4. Look at verse three.
Find and **copy two words** that show that soldiers are unable to carry on the fight.

1. ___ 2. ___

5. **Find** and **copy a phrase** that tells the reader that they must not break their promise to continue trying to defeat the enemy.

___

6. Look at this line from the last verse:
"If ye break faith with us who die
We shall not sleep,"
Which of the following could replace the phrase *"shall not sleep"* while keeping the same meaning? **Circle one.**

will not go to bed	will walk around	will not be at peace	will dream

Retrieval

In Flanders Fields

1. Between which objects are the poppies growing?

____

2. Where in the country of Belgium have the soldiers been buried?

____

3. Why can't the larks be heard down on the ground?

____

4. Why are the soldiers passing on the torch?

____

5. Using information from the text, put a tick in the correct box to show whether each statement is **true** or **false**.

	True	**False**
The war continues on the ground.		
The graves are marked with angels.		
The soldiers died weeks ago.		
The soldiers are at peace		

In Flanders Fields

1. Think about the whole poem. **Which phrase** best summarises what the poem is about?

	Tick **one**
Nature versus War	
Sacrifice	
Life and Death	
Hope for the Future	

Explain your choice **using evidence** from the text.

Inference — In Flanders Fields

1. Look at these lines from the first verse:

"and in the sky
The larks still bravely singing, fly
Scarce heard amid the guns below."

What do the larks and the guns symbolise?

larks ______________________________

guns ______________________________

2. Look at these lines from the second verse:

"We lived, felt dawn, saw sunset glow
Loved and were loved"

What do these lines tell you about the men speaking in the poem?

____

____

3. Explain what the author means by *"The torch"* in the lines below.

"To you from failing hands we throw
The torch; be yours to hold it high"

____

____

4. Draw lines to match each phrase with what it shows you about the soldiers.

Phrases		The Soldiers
Loved and were loved		Death was sudden
Now we lie		They have died
Saw sunset glow		Had friends and families at home
Short days ago		Lived each day beginning to end

5. Which verse gives a message for the future? **Tick one**.

Verse One		Verse Two		Verse Three	

Prediction

In Flanders Fields

1. The poet, John McCrae, was a doctor during the First World War. He wrote this poem just after a friend was killed. How do you think other soldiers might have felt after hearing this poem? Refer to the poem in your answer.

Text Meaning In Flanders Fields

1. This poem has a strong rhythm. Why do you think the poet chose to make the poem so rhythmical? What impact does it have on the reader?

____

____

2. Draw lines to match each part of the poem with the correct poetic technique.

rhyme	In Flanders fields
metaphor	In Flanders fields the poppies blow Between the crosses row on row,
repetition	We lived, felt dawn, saw sunset glow
imagery	To you from failing hands we throw The torch...

3. Write the words from the poem to complete the pairs of rhyming words.

blow	
high	
ago	
throw	

Author's Use of Language — In Flanders Fields

1. John McCrae was a Canadian doctor during the First World War. This poem has not been written from his point of view. Who is the voice in this poem?

____

____

2. What is the purpose of repeating the phrase *"In Flanders fields"*?

____

____

3. How is personification used in verse one?

____

____

4. In verse three, the poet speaks directly to the reader. Why does he do this? What is the impact on the reader?

____

____

____

____

5. This poem was written in 1915. Why has it stood the test of time and what makes it still one of the most well-known remembrance poems?

____

____

____

____

Compare and Contrast — In Flanders Fields

1. *"The larks still bravely singing, fly*
Scarce heard amid the guns below."

These two lines of poetry create two very different images. How do they differ?

____

____

____

____

____

2. The poet uses imagery to paint a picture for the reader.
a) How does the imagery differ in these two quotes from verse two?
We are the Dead

We lived, felt dawn, saw sunset glow
Loved and were loved

____

____

____

____

____

____

b) What does this contrast show the reader?

____

____

____

Leisure

by W.H. Davies

WHAT is this life if, full of care,
We have no time to stand and stare? –

No time to stand beneath the boughs,
And stare as long as sheep and cows:

No time to see, when woods we pass,
Where squirrels hide their nuts in grass:

No time to see, in broad daylight,
Streams full of stars, like skies at night:

No time to turn at Beauty's glance,
And watch her feet, how they can dance:

No time to wait till her mouth can
Enrich that smile her eyes began?

A poor life this if, full of care,
We have no time to stand and stare.

Vocabulary Leisure

1. *"No time to stand beneath the boughs,"*

Circle the correct word to complete the line below:

There is no time to stand beneath the ____________

stars	branches
bows	arches

2. **Find** and **copy two words or phrases** that give a clue about the time of day.

1. ____________________

2. ____________________

3. Explain what the expression *"in broad daylight"* means.

____

4. *"No time to turn at Beauty's glance"*

Which word is closest in meaning to **glance**?

	Tick **one**
face	
blink	
stare	
glimpse	

5. **Find** and **copy one word** that is closest in meaning to add value.

____

6. **Find** and **copy a phrase** that could be replaced with stop and look.

____

Retrieval   Leisure

1. Which image was NOT created in this poem? **Circle one**.

2. At the beginning of the poem, what does the narrator wish everyone had more time to do?

____

3. Which animals does the narrator envy? **Find** and **copy two**.

1. ______________________
2. ______________________

4. In the second half of the poem, the narrator compares beauty in life to a woman. What **two** things does he appreciate about her?

1. ______________________
2. ______________________

5. Using information from the poem, put a tick in the correct box to show whether each statement is **true** or **false**.

	True	False
The narrator doesn't have time to wait for happiness in the eyes to turn into a smile.		
The narrator feels life is very rich.		
People often have to rush through the woods.		
The narrator looks at the stream at night.		

Summary Leisure

1. Another possible title for this poem could be *"Stop and Smell the Roses."* **Write two** or **three sentences** explaining whether you agree with this or not and why.

2. Which **two** statements are not key messages of this poem?

	Tick **two**
It is important to work hard and keep busy.	
Take time to enjoy the simple things in life.	
Don't rush through life and miss all the beauty.	
Don't be lazy and waste time relaxing.	

3. This poem was first published in 1911. Are the main messages of this poem still appropriate for life now? Explain your answer.

Inference Leisure

1. Why are the people passing the squirrels in the woods so quickly? Where might they be going?

____

____

____

____

2. Who might Beauty be?

____

3. **Find** and **copy three** pieces of evidence the narrator gives to prove that people's lives are too *"full of care"*.

1. ______________________

2. ______________________

3. ______________________

4. Put a tick in the correct box to show whether each of the following statements is a **fact** or **opinion**.

	Fact	Opinion
Everyone should stop and take time to enjoy nature.		
People's lives are very busy with work and families.		
A smile is very beautiful.		
Sheep and cows do not have the same responsibilities as people.		

5. *"A poor life this if, full of care,*
We have no time to stand and stare."
What impression do these final lines of the poem give you of what the narrator believes about life?

____

Prediction Leisure

1. After reflecting on his life, how might the narrator make changes to how he spends his time?
Make a reasonable prediction with reference to the poem.

____

____

____

____

____

____

2. In this poem, the narrator names a number things that make him happy and he wants to make more time for. What are some things that make you happy that you need to prioritise time for in your life? Why is this important to you?

____

____

____

____

____

____

Text Meaning   Leisure

1. a) What is the rhyme scheme of this poem?

____

1. b) What is this type of rhyme scheme usually called?

____

2. Write the words from the poem to complete the pairs of rhyming words.

care	
pass	
daylight	
can	

Author's Use of Language   Leisure

1. The phrase *"No time"* is repeated seven times in this poem. What is the intended effect of repeating it so many times?

____

____

____

2. **Find** and **copy three examples** of **alliteration** in this poem.

1. ______________________________
2. ______________________________
3. ______________________________

3. *"Streams full of stars, like skies at night."*
What impression does this give you of the stream?

____

____

4. In the second half of the poem, the poet uses personification.
How is beauty personified? To what is it being compared?

____

____

5. *"A poor life this if, full of care,"*

What does this phrase A poor life suggest about the life of most people?

____

____

Compare and Contrast

Leisure

1. Why does the narrator compare being able to *"stand and stare"* to sheep and cows?

____

____

2. How are streams in broad daylight and the night sky similar?

____

____

3. How does the narrator hope people's lives will change?

____

____

In the Bleak Midwinter

by Christina Rossetti

In the bleak mid-winter, frosty wind made moan,
Earth stood hard as iron, water like a stone;
Snow had fallen, snow on snow, snow on snow,
In the bleak mid-winter, long ago.

Our God, Heaven cannot hold Him, nor earth sustain;
Heaven and earth shall flee away when He comes to reign.
In the bleak mid-winter a stable place sufficed
The Lord God Almighty, Jesus Christ.

Enough for Him, whom cherubim, worship night and day,
Breastful of milk, and a mangerful of hay;
Enough for Him whom Angels fall down before,
The ox and ass and camel which adore.

Angels and archangels may have gathered there,
Cherubim and seraphim thronged the air;
But His mother only, in her maiden bliss,
Worshipped the beloved with a kiss.

What can I give Him, poor as I am?
If I were a Shepherd, I would bring a lamb;
If I were a Wise Man, I would do my part;
Yet what I can I give Him: give my heart.

Did you know this poem was also a Christmas carol?
Try listening to the carol to help with your understanding.

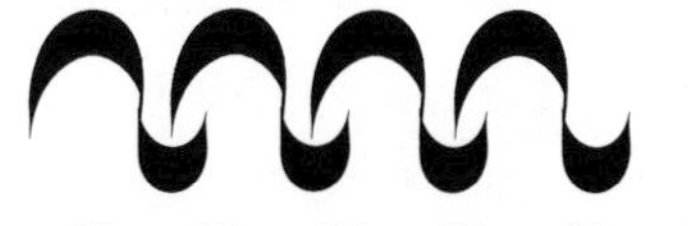

Vocabulary In the Bleak Midwinter

1. This poem has the title *"In the Bleak Midwinter"*.

Which **other word** could the poet use to describe midwinter?

Tick **one**			
long		empty	
bright		dreary	

2. *"heaven cannot hold Him / nor earth sustain,"*

Which word is closest in meaning to sustain?

Tick **one**			
support		ignore	
condemn		neglect	

3. In the second stanza, **find** and **copy one word** that tells us the stable was enough for Jesus.

____

4. In this poem, there are three other words for angels. Write them below.

1. ______________________________
2. ______________________________
3. ______________________________

5. *"Cherubim and Seraphim / Thronged the air;"*

What does thronged the air mean in this line?

____

____

6. **Find** and **copy a group of words** that show the narrator will make a contribution.

____

Retrieval

In the Bleak Midwinter

Circle the correct answer for each question:

1. What time of year is this poem set?

summer	winter	Easter	autumn

2. How much snow was on the ground?

just a sprinkle	none at all	piles of snow	it was raining

3. Where did the baby come from?

Earth	Heaven	the stable	angels

4. Who was born in the stable?

Mary	a lamb	a shepherd	Jesus

5. Why is the narrator unsure about what gift to give to Jesus?

She doesn't know what he would like.	She is poor.	Jesus already has a lot of gifts.	She is a Wise Man and knows what to bring.

6. What was the mother's gift to her son?

a kiss	milk and a manger of hay	a lamb	angels

7. What might a shepherd bring as a gift?

gold	a mangerful of hay	his heart	a lamb

8. What does the narrator decide to give Jesus in the end?

a kiss	her heart	a lamb	gold, frankincense and myrrh

In the Bleak Midwinter

1. Which of the following is a group of themes for this poem? **Circle one**.

Death / Loss / Sadness	Hope / Peace / Happiness
Mother's Love / Nativity / Gifts	Nature / Animals / Spring

2. Below are summaries of each stanza of this poem. **Number them 1 – 5** to show the order in which they appear in the text. The first one has been done for you.

Simple comforts were enough for him.	
Angels gathered around as his mother loved him.	
The world was cold and still.	1
Powerful Jesus came to earth.	
Gifts for the baby.	

Inference In the Bleak Midwinter

1. At the beginning of the poem, it is very cold. **List four ways** the poet shows this.

1. ______________________________
2. ______________________________
3. ______________________________
4. ______________________________

2. *"... Heaven cannot hold Him, nor earth sustain:"*
What does this line tell the reader about the power of God?

____

____

3. What does the third verse tell the reader about where Jesus was born?
Use evidence from the text to support your answer.

____

____

4. **What evidence** is there that he was a very important baby?

____

____

5. What is **special** about his mother in the fourth stanza?

____

____

Prediction

In the Bleak Midwinter

1. In 1906, this poem was turned into a hymn with music by Gustav Holst. It was very popular during the First World War. Why do you think this was? **Make reference** to the poem in your answer.

Text Meaning In the Bleak Midwinter

1. What is the rhyme scheme of this poem?

____

2. This poem became a well-known Christmas carol. What is it about the rhyme scheme that helped it become an effective song?

____

3. How does the final stanza differ from the rest of the poem?

____

Author's Use of Language

In the Bleak Midwinter

1. **Alliteration** is a common poetic technique. **Find** and **copy an example** of alliteration in the first stanza.

____

2. **Assonance** is similar to alliteration. It is a repeated vowel sound found in the middle of words. **Find** and **copy a phrase** that is an example of assonance in the first stanza.

____

3. **Find** and **copy two similes** found in this poem.

1. ____

2. ____

4. *"Heaven and earth shall flee away..."*

Which literary device is this an example of?

____

5. *"... whom Angels fall before"*

What does this description suggest about the scene?

____

____

6. In the final line of the poem, the narrator says she will "*Give her heart*". What does this **metaphor** actually mean?

____

____

Compare and Contrast

In the Bleak Midwinter

1. How does the description of the stable in stanza three compare with the title Jesus is given in the last line of stanza two?

____

____

2. How does his mother differ from everyone else in the poem?

____

3. a) How is the narrator similar to the shepherd and Wise Man?

____

b) How is the narrator different from the shepherd and Wise Man?

____

4. In what way are the narrator and Jesus' mother similar?

____

The Way Through the Woods

by Rudyard Kipling

They shut the road through the woods
Seventy years ago.
Weather and rain have undone it again,
And now you would never know
There was once a road through the woods
Before they planted the trees.
It is underneath the coppice and heath,
And the thin anemones.
Only the keeper sees
That, where the ring-dove broods,
And the badgers roll at ease,
There was once a road through the woods.

Yet, if you enter the woods
Of a summer evening late,
When the night-air cools on the trout-ringed pools
Where the otter whistles his mate,
(They fear not men in the woods,
Because they see so few.)
You will hear the beat of a horse's feet,
And the swish of a skirt in the dew,
Steadily cantering through
The misty solitudes,
As though they perfectly knew
The old lost road through the woods.
But there is no road through the woods.

Vocabulary The Way Through the Woods

1. Look at the beginning of the poem. **Find** and **copy a phrase** that tells the reader that the natural elements have pretty much erased the road.

____

2. Look at the first stanza. **Find** and **copy two words** that describe different kinds of growth in the woods.

1. ______________________________

2. ______________________________

3. *"It is underneath the coppice and heath, / And the thin anemones."*
Which word is a variety of flowers?

	Tick **one**
anemones	
underneath	
coppice	
heath	

4. In the first stanza, **find** and **copy a group of words** that tell you the animals are quite relaxed.

____

5. **Find** and **copy a word** that tells you how fast the horse is moving.

____

6. *"Steadily cantering through / The misty solitudes"*
Which word is closest in meaning to solitudes?

	Tick **one**
trees	
silence	
paths	

Retrieval — The Way Through the Woods

1. How long ago was there a road through the woods?

____

2. What did they do to get rid of the road through the woods?

____

3. Who is the only person who gets to see the beauty of the woods?

____

4. Why don't the otters and other animals fear people?

____

5. **Find** and **copy two** things you might hear but wouldn't expect if you go into the woods late in the evening.

1. ____

2. ____

6. Using information from the poem, put a tick in the correct box to show whether each statement is **true** or **false**.

	True	False
You might see hedgehogs in the woods.		
Birds are raising their babies in the woods.		
The summer evenings are very warm.		
It is very quiet in the woods at night.		

Summary

The Way Through the Woods

1. Which of the following is a theme of this poem?

	Tick **one**
Friendship	
The power of nature	
Love	
Building and development	

2. Below are some summaries of different parts of this poem. **Number them 1–6** to show the order in which they appear in the text. The first one has been done for you.

In the misty silence, no one is there and there is no road through the woods.	
The animals are relaxed and unafraid.	
On summer evenings, you might hear the sound of someone who once rode through the woods.	
Only the keeper is able to visit the beauty of nature in the woods.	
They manage the growth of the woods by planting trees, cutting some back and letting other areas grow wild.	
They shut the road through the woods.	**1**

Inference The Way Through the Woods

1. How old is the narrator of this poem? **Use evidence** from the text to support your answer.

___

___

2. **What impression** do you get of the keeper? Refer to the text in your answer.

___

___

3. Why do the woods appeal to the narrator? **Use evidence** from the text in your answer.

___

___

___

___

4. How has life changed for the animals in the woods? Refer to the text in your answer.

___

___

___

Inference The Way Through the Woods

5. The woods seem to have a memory of the road that was once there. **What evidence** is there of this statement in the poem?

____

____

____

____

6. Put a tick in the correct box to show whether each of the following statements is a **fact** or **opinion**.

	Fact	Opinion
The woods are better without the road.		
The air is cooler in the evening.		
Otters and badgers live in the woods.		
There are ghosts in the woods.		

Prediction   The Way Through the Woods

1. Should the road through the woods be restored?

	Tick **one**
yes	
no	

Use evidence from the poem to support your opinion.

____

____

____

____

____

____

2. Based on what you have read, what will happen to the animals if the woods are left as they are now?

Make a reasonable prediction with reference to the poem.

____

____

____

____

____

____

Text Meaning The Way Through the Woods

1. Write the words from the poem to complete the pairs of rhyming words.

ago	
late	
dew	
trees	

2. This poem contains four lines with internal rhymes.

Find and **copy two** of these lines below and **circle** the internal rhymes.

1. ______________________________

____

2. ______________________________

____

Author's Use of Language

The Way Through the Woods

1. Which of the following lines from the poem is an example of **personification**?

	Tick **one**
Weather and rain have undone it again	
Before they planted the trees	
There was once a road through the woods	
You will hear the beat of a horse's feet	

2. *"They shut the road through the woods*
Seventy years ago."

By making this statement, how does the author want the reader to feel? Explain your answer with because.

____

____

3. *"When the night-air cools on the trout-ringed pools"*

Give **two impressions** this gives you of the woods at night.

1. ____

2. ____

4. *"Where the otter whistles his mate"*

What **impression** does the line give you of the otter?

____

____

5. **Find** and **copy one phrase** that gives the impression that the woods are isolated and still.

____

Compare and Contrast

The Way Through the Woods

1. How have the woods changed in the last 70 years?

____

____

2. *"They fear not men in the woods, Because they see so few."*

How are the animals' reactions to people different now compared to when there was a road through the woods?

____

____

3. The mood of the poem changes in the last half of the second stanza. **What impression** does the poet give of the woods now? Make reference to the poem in your answer.

____

____

____

____

"Hope" is the Thing with Feathers

by Emily Dickinson

"Hope" is the thing with feathers –
That perches in the soul –
And sings the tune without the words –
And never stops – at all –

And sweetest – in the Gale – is heard –
And sore must be the storm –
That could abash the little Bird
That kept so many warm –

I've heard it in the chillest land –
And on the strangest Sea –
Yet – never – in Extremity,
It asked a crumb – of me.

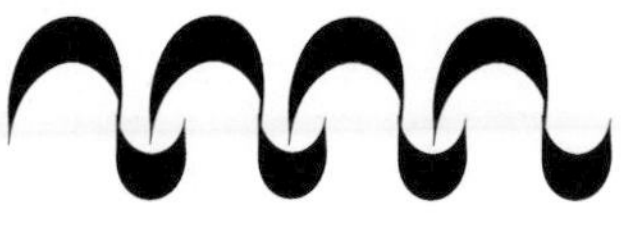

Vocabulary "Hope" is the Thing with Feathers

1. **Find** and **copy one word** from the first verse that tells how the thing with feathers is sitting.

____

2. *"And sore must be the storm"*
Which word is closest in meaning to sore?

	Tick **one**
weak	
hurt	
severe	
long	

3. **Find** and **copy one word** from the second verse that means to embarrass, humiliate or shame.

____

4. Look at the final verse. In your **own words**, explain what a situation that is known as an *Extremity*, might be like.

____

____

5. *"Yet – never – in Extremity,/ It asked a crumb – of me."*

What does the word crumb tell you about what the bird expected in return for its help?

	Tick **one**
It expected much in return	
It expected payment in bread	
It spoke to the narrator about how much it liked crumbs	
It expected very little in return	

Retrieval

"Hope" is the Thing with Feathers

1. **Circle** the correct options to complete the sentences below:

a) Hope is being compared to a ________________

feather	butterfly
bird	squirrel

b) It can be found in ________________

the soul	the mind
the air	the feelings

2. Using information from the text, put a tick in the correct box to show whether each statement is **true** or **false**.

	True	False
Hope sounds best in fierce winds.		
Hope stops singing when the person has enough.		
Hope keeps people warm.		
Hope asks for payment.		

3. Look at the third verse.

Where has the narrator heard hope singing?

1. ____

2. ____

Summary "Hope" is the Thing with Feathers

1. Which of the following is a theme for this poem?

	Tick **one**
Hope Eternal	
Friendship with Animals	
Love	
Persevering in Suffering	

2. Below are some summaries of different parts of this poem. **Number them 1 – 4** to show the order in which they appear in the poem. The first one has been done for you.

Hope survives in many difficult situations.	
Hope's song is described.	
Hope asks for nothing in return.	
The metaphor of Hope as a bird is introduced.	**1**

3. Fill in the blanks to complete this sentence about the poem.

Birds cannot fly without ______________________ ;

people cannot live without ______________________ .

Inference "Hope" is the Thing with Feathers

1. a) This poem is an extended metaphor for hope. To what is hope being compared?

___

b) **Find** and **copy the line** from the poem that confirms this **metaphor**.

___

2. **Find** and **copy three** pieces of evidence from the first verse that give clues to the metaphor (how do you know?).

1. ___
2. ___
3. ___

3. Where is the bird's home?

___

4. What is life like for the narrator of the poem? **Give evidence** from the poem to support your answer.

___

___

___

___

5. How does the bird's song make people feel?

___

___

Prediction "Hope" is the Thing with Feathers

1. Give an example of a time in your life when you might need this bird.
Make references to the poem in your answer.

Text Meaning "Hope" is the Thing with Feathers

1. What is the rhyme scheme of this poem? Verse one has been done for you.

Verse one: ABCB

Verse two: __________

Verse three: __________

2. Apart from the first line, there is a consistent rhythm to this poem. The number of syllables in each line follows a pattern.

a) What is the pattern?

____

b) What impact does this rhythm have on how the poem sounds?

____

3. In what person is this poem written? How do you know?

____

Author's Use of Language

"Hope" is the Thing with Feathers

1. *"And sings the tunes without the words"*

What is the significance of the tune having no words?

____

2. **Find** and **copy the phrase** from the **first** verse that tells the reader that Hope is everlasting.

____

3. **Find** and **copy the phrase** from the **second** verse that tells the reader that Hope is not just for the narrator of the poem.

____

4. Emily Dickinson, the poet, uses many literary devices in this poem.

Draw lines to match each phrase to the correct literary device.

alliteration	Hope is the thing with feathers
personification	That perches in the soul
consonance	And sore must be the storm
alliteration	And on the strangest Sea

5. This poem is full of **symbolism**.

Find and **copy four words or phrases** that **symbolise** hard times in life.

1. ______________ 2. ______________

3. ______________ 4. ______________

Compare and Contrast

"Hope" is the Thing with Feathers

1. This poem is an **extended metaphor** comparing two things. What two things are being compared?

2. Hope is an **abstract noun** while bird is a concrete noun.
How does this comparison help the reader to understand Hope?

3. In the second verse, how is 'Hope's' song different from the situation the narrator is in?

The Highwayman

by Alfred Noyes

Part One

The wind was a torrent of darkness among the gusty trees.
The moon was a ghostly galleon tossed upon cloudy seas.
The road was a ribbon of moonlight over the purple moor,
And the highwayman came riding—
Riding—riding—
The highwayman came riding, up to the old inn-door.

He'd a French cocked-hat on his forehead, a bunch of lace at his chin,
A coat of the claret velvet, and breeches of brown doe-skin.
They fitted with never a wrinkle. His boots were up to the thigh.
And he rode with a jewelled twinkle,
His pistol butts a-twinkle,
His rapier hilt a-twinkle, under the jewelled sky.

Over the cobbles he clattered and clashed in the dark inn-yard.
He tapped with his whip on the shutters, but all was locked and barred.
He whistled a tune to the window, and who should be waiting there
But the landlord's black-eyed daughter,
Bess, the landlord's daughter,
Plaiting a dark red love-knot into her long black hair.

And dark in the dark old inn-yard a stable-wicket creaked
Where Tim the ostler listened. His face was white and peaked.
His eyes were hollows of madness, his hair like mouldy hay,
But he loved the landlord's daughter,
        The landlord's red-lipped daughter.
Dumb as a dog he listened, and he heard the robber say—

"One kiss, my bonny sweetheart, I'm after a prize to-night,
But I shall be back with the yellow gold before the morning light;
Yet, if they press me sharply, and harry me through the day,
Then look for me by moonlight,
        Watch for me by moonlight,
I'll come to thee by moonlight, though hell should bar the way."

He rose upright in the stirrups; he scarce could reach her hand,
But she loosened her hair in the casement. His face burnt like a brand
As the black cascade of perfume came tumbling over his breast;
And he kissed its waves in the moonlight,
        (O, sweet black waves in the moonlight!)
Then he tugged at his rein in the moonlight, and galloped away to the west.

Part Two

He did not come in the dawning. He did not come at noon;
And out of the tawny sunset, before the rise of the moon,
When the road was a gypsy's ribbon, looping the purple moor,
A red-coat troop came marching—
Marching—marching—
King George's men came marching, up to the old inn-door.

They said no word to the landlord. They drank his ale instead.
But they gagged his daughter and bound her, to the foot of her narrow bed.
Two of them knelt at her casement, with muskets at their side!
There was death at every window;
And hell at one dark window;
For Bess could see, through her casement, the road that *he* would ride.

They had tied her up to attention, with many a sniggering jest.
They had bound a musket beside her, with the muzzle beneath her breast!
"Now, keep good watch!" and they kissed her. She heard the doomed man say—
Look for me by moonlight;
Watch for me by moonlight;
I'll come to thee by moonlight, though hell should bar the way!

She twisted her hands behind her; but all the knots held good!
She writhed her hands till her fingers were wet with sweat or blood!
They stretched and strained in the darkness, and the hours crawled by like years
Till, now, on the stroke of midnight,
Cold, on the stroke of midnight,
The tip of one finger touched it! The trigger at least was hers!

The tip of one finger touched it. She strove no more for the rest.
Up, she stood up to attention, with the muzzle beneath her breast.
She would not risk their hearing; she would not strive again;
For the road lay bare in the moonlight;
    Blank and bare in the moonlight;
And the blood of her veins in the moonlight throbbed to her love's refrain.

Tlot-tlot; tlot-tlot! Had they heard it? The horsehoofs ringing clear;
Tlot-tlot; tlot-tlot, in the distance? Were they deaf that they did not hear?
Down the ribbon of moonlight, over the brow of the hill,
The highwayman came riding—
    Riding—riding—
The red coats looked to their priming! She stood up, straight and still!

Tlot-tlot, in the frosty silence! tlot-tlot, in the echoing night!
Nearer he came and nearer! Her face was like a light!
Her eyes grew wide for a moment; she drew one last deep breath,
Then her finger moved in the moonlight,
    Her musket shattered the moonlight,
Shattered her breast in the moonlight and warned him—with her death.

He turned; he spurred to the west; he did not know who stood
Bowed, with her head o'er the musket, drenched with her own blood!
Not till the dawn he heard it, and slowly blanched to hear
How Bess, the landlord's daughter,
    The landlord's black-eyed daughter,
Had watched for her love in the moonlight, and died in the darkness there.

Back, he spurred like a madman, shrieking a curse to the sky,
With the white road smoking behind him and his rapier brandished high!
Blood-red were his spurs in the golden noon; wine-red was his velvet coat;
When they shot him down on the highway,
        Down like a dog on the highway,
And he lay in his blood on the highway, with a bunch of lace at his throat.

****

And still of a winter's night, they say, when the wind is in the trees,
When the moon is a ghostly galleon tossed upon cloudy seas,
When the road is a ribbon of moonlight over the purple moor,
A highwayman comes riding—
        Riding—riding—
A highwayman comes riding, up to the old inn-door.

Over the cobbles he clatters and clangs in the dark inn-yard.
He taps with his whip on the shutters, but all is locked and barred.
He whistles a tune to the window, and who should be waiting there
But the landlord's black-eyed daughter,
        Bess, the landlord's daughter,
Plaiting a dark red love-knot into her long black hair.

Vocabulary The Highwayman

1. *"The moon was a ghostly galleon tossed upon cloudy seas,"*

Explain two things the words ghostly galleon suggest about the moon.

____

____

2. Look at Part One.

Find and **copy one word** that is closest in meaning to window.

____

3. *"As the black cascade of perfume came tumbling over his breast;"*

Which word is closest in meaning to cascade?

	Tick **one**
cloud	
wave	
waterfall	
waft	

4. **Find** and **copy one phrase** that shows the soldiers were laughing about Bess and the Highwayman.

____

5. **Find** and **copy two verbs** that show that Bess was trying to free her hands.

1. ____

2. ____

6. **Find** and **copy a group of words** that tell you that once she touched the trigger, Bess wasn't going to try to move her hands any more in case the soldiers heard her.

____

Retrieval The Highwayman

1. **Circle** the correct option to complete each sentence below.

a) The Highwayman left Bess to

rob a bank	steal gold	break into an inn	win a prize

b) When the soldiers tied up Bess, she was

sitting in a chair	sitting on the bed	standing very straight	standing in the corner

c) After the Highwayman heard of Bess' death and he returned to the inn, he was killed

at dawn	at midnight	at sunset	at noon

d) The ghosts of the Highwayman and Bess still meet

on a winter's night	at midnight	in the wind	on the purple moor

2. What are the two weapons the Highwayman carries with him?

_______________ _______________

3. Write down **three** things you are told about Tim.

1. _______________
2. _______________
3. _______________

4. What was Tim doing at the stable door?

____

Retrieval — The Highwayman

5. Look at Part Two.

Find and **copy four things** the soldiers did that were inappropriate when they arrived at the inn.

1. ______________________________

2. ______________________________

3. ______________________________

4. ______________________________

6. How did Bess warn the Highwayman about the soldiers?

____

7. **Find** and **copy three pieces** of evidence that tell us The Highwayman is set in the 18th century.

1. ______________________________

2. ______________________________

3. ______________________________

8. Using information from the text, put a tick in the correct box to show whether each statement is **true** or **false**.

	True	False
The Highwayman knew Tim was listening		
The Highwayman was on horseback		
The soldiers worked for King Edward		
The soldiers stole money from the landlord		

Summary The Highwayman

1. Which of the following best describes the main message of this poem?

	Tick **one**
Criminals will pay in the end	
Stay away from criminals	
True love lasts forever	
Love is worth dying for	

2. Below are some summaries of different parts of this text. **Number them 1–6** to show the order in which they appear in the text. The first one has been done for you.

Soldiers came to the inn to wait for the Highwayman.	
Tim listened from the stable.	
The Highwayman promised to return with gold.	
Bess killed herself to warn the Highwayman.	
The Highwayman visited Bess at the inn.	**1**
The Highwayman returned to the inn to avenge Bess' death.	

Inference The Highwayman

1. Why did the Highwayman whistle instead of calling out to Bess?

____

____

2. Read the verse beginning *"And dark in the dark old inn-yard a stable-wicket creaked..."*
What impression is given of Tim's character? Use evidence from the poem to support your answer.

____

____

____

____

3. *"And the blood of her veins in the moonlight throbbed to her love's refrain."*
What does this line suggest about Bess' feelings?

____

____

4. Look at the verse beginning *"Tlot-tlot in the frosty silence..."*
Find and **copy a phrase** that is used to show Bess' fear.

____

____

5. *"Shattered her breast in the moonlight and warned him—with her death."*
What does this line suggest about Bess' character?

____

____

6. How did the Highwayman feel when he heard about Bess' death? Explain how you know.

____

____

Prediction The Highwayman

1. Based on what you have read, what do you think happened to Tim after Bess' death?
Use **evidence** from the poem to support your prediction.

____

____

____

____

____

____

2. Who should be blamed for Bess' death? **Circle one.**

The Highwayman	Tim	Bess	The Soldiers	The Landlord

Explain your opinion with reasons from the poem.

____

____

____

____

____

____

Text Meaning The Highwayman

1. Draw lines to match each poetic technique with the correct quotation from the poem.

repetition	dark red love-knot
onomatopoeia	Tlot tlot
simile	The road was a ribbon of moonlight
metaphor	riding—riding—riding
symbolism	Down like a dog on the highway

2. This poem is divided into three sections: Part One, Part Two and an epilogue. Why has the poet done this?

____

____

____

____

____

____

Author's Use of Language The Highwayman

1. The poet uses a lot of **imagery** in the first verse. What does the language suggest about the night?

____

____

____

____

____

____

2. **Find** and **copy two examples** of a **simile** used to describe Tim.

1. ____

2. ____

3. *"I'll come to thee by moonlight, though hell should bar the way."*
The poet is using a **metaphor** in this line. What might stop the Highwayman from returning to Bess?

____

____

4. *"...the hours crawled by like years"*
What does this description suggest about Bess' thoughts?

____

____

____

Author's Use of Language — The Highwayman

5. *"Her musket shattered the moonlight,*
Shattered her breast in the moonlight and warned him—with her death."

What impression does this give of the gunshot?

____

____

6. *"Plaiting a dark red love-knot into her long black hair".*

This is used throughout the poem as a symbol of the love between Bess and the Highwayman. What does this description suggest about their love?

____

____

7. The poet uses the colour red throughout the poem.

a) What **two** things could the colour red symbolise?

1. ______________________

2. ______________________

b) **Find four places** where the colour red is used.

1. ______________________

2. ______________________

3. ______________________

4. ______________________

Compare and Contrast The Highwayman

1. In the first three verses, the character of the Highwayman is introduced.
Which **two words** show the contrast between the Highwayman and the inn-yard?

The Highwayman: ______________________________

The inn-yard: ______________________________

2. The characters of Bess and Tim are introduced in Part One.
Give **two** ways Bess and Tim are different.

1. ______________________________
2. ______________________________

3. In the epilogue of the poem, Bess and the Highwayman are together again.
How do you think their relationship will be similar to and different from when they were alive?

____

____

____

____

____

____

The Listeners

by Walter de la Mare

'Is there anybody there?' said the Traveller,
  Knocking on the moonlit door;
And his horse in the silence champed the grasses
  Of the forest's ferny floor:
And a bird flew up out of the turret,
  Above the Traveller's head:
And he smote upon the door again a second time;
  'Is there anybody there?' he said.
But no one descended to the Traveller;
  No head from the leaf-fringed sill
Leaned over and looked into his grey eyes,
  Where he stood perplexed and still.
But only a host of phantom listeners
  That dwelt in the lone house then
Stood listening in the quiet of the moonlight
  To that voice from the world of men:
Stood thronging the faint moonbeams on the dark stair,
  That goes down to the empty hall,
Hearkening in an air stirred and shaken
  By the lonely Traveller's call.
And he felt in his heart their strangeness,
  Their stillness answering his cry,
While his horse moved, cropping the dark turf,
  'Neath the starred and leafy sky;
For he suddenly smote on the door, even

Louder, and lifted his head:—
'Tell them I came, and no one answered,
That I kept my word,' he said.
Never the least stir made the listeners,
Though every word he spake
Fell echoing through the shadowiness of the still house
From the one man left awake:
Ay, they heard his foot upon the stirrup,
And the sound of iron on stone,
And how the silence surged softly backward,
When the plunging hoofs were gone.

Vocabulary The Listeners

1. **Find** and **copy one word** that tells the reader the man knocked on the door forcefully.

____

2. *"Where he stood perplexed and still."*

Which word is closest in meaning to perplexed?

	Tick **one**
quiet	
confused	
frightened	
alone	

3. Look at the section of the poem about the listeners inside the house.
Find and **copy two words** that show there were many listeners.

1. ______________________________

2. ______________________________

4. **Find** and **copy one synonym** for listening.

____

5. *"When his horse moved, cropping the dark turf,"*

What was the horse doing?

	Tick **one**
Waiting for his master	
Eating the grass	
Stamping the grass	
Cutting the grass	

6. *"And how the silence surged softly backward,"*

What does surged softly backward mean?

____

Retrieval # The Listeners

1. Which of these best represents the house? **Circle one**.

2. Write down **three** things the reader is told about the house.

1. ______________________________
2. ______________________________
3. ______________________________

3. Who stood listening inside the house?

____

4. How many times did the Traveller knock in total?

____

5. What was revealed about the Traveller?

	Tick **one**
He had seen someone in the house.	
He once lived in the house.	
Someone had sent him to the house.	
He had made a promise to someone in the house.	

Summary The Listeners

1. People cannot always find the answers they are looking for no matter how hard they look.

Is this statement a good summary of the poem? Explain your answer with reference to the poem.

____

____

____

____

2. Below are some summaries of different parts of this poem. **Number them 1–6** to show the order in which they appear in the text. The first one has been done for you.

The Traveller knocked on the door but no one came.	
The phantoms heard the Traveller leave.	
The Traveller knocked on the door as a bird flew away.	1
No one looked out the window at the Traveller.	
The Listeners gathered on the stair.	
The Traveller cried out that he had kept his word to come.	

Inference The Listeners

1. What does the Traveller's name tell the reader about him?

___

___

2. **What evidence** is there that nature is taking over the house?

___

___

3. What time of day does the Traveller arrive at the house? How do you know?

___

4. **Find** and **copy one phrase** that tells the reader the inhabitants of the house are from a different world to the Traveller.

___

Inference The Listeners

5. **Find** and **copy one line** from the poem that tells the reader the Traveller knew the Listeners were there.

___

6. From what you know about the Traveller, why has he come to the house? **Use evidence** from the poem to support your answer.

___
___
___
___
___
___

7. *"Their stillness answering his cry,"*
What does this line suggest about the listeners?

___
___
___

Prediction The Listeners

1. What will the Traveller do next? **Use evidence** from the poem to support your prediction.

2. What connection could the Traveller have to the house? What could have happened there?

Text Meaning The Listeners

1. Draw lines to match each poetic technique with the correct quotation from the poem.

alliteration	The stillness answering his cry,
onomatopoeia	Of the forest's ferny floor:
personification	Hearkening in an air stirred and shaken
Imagery	And his horse in the silence champed the grasses

Author's Use of Language

The Listeners

1. **Find** and **copy four different words** from the poem that help to build up the eerie atmosphere of the poem.

1. ______________________
2. ______________________
3. ______________________
4. ______________________

2. *"No head from the leaf-fringed sill"*

What does the phrase leaf-fringed sill tell the reader about the house?

____

3. *"Leaned over and looked into his grey eyes,"*

What does this line suggest about the Traveller's emotions?

____

____

4. One of the themes of the poem is silence.

Find and **copy three words or phrases** that support this theme.

1. ______________________
2. ______________________
3. ______________________

5. *"Hearkening in an air stirred and shaken*
By the lonely Traveller's call."

What does this description suggest about the setting?

____

____

____

Author's Use of Language The Listeners

6. The poet, Walter de la Mare, uses a lot of alliteration in this poem.
Find and **copy three** examples of **alliteration**.

1. ____________________
2. ____________________
3. ____________________

7. What is the effect of the use of alliteration? What does it sound like?

____

____

8. *"For he suddenly smote on the door, even*
Louder, and lifted his head: -"

What does this tell the reader about the attitude of the Traveller?

____

9. *"Fell echoing through the shadowiness of the still house"*
What does this description suggest about the Traveller's call?

____

____

____

10. *"When the plunging hoofs were gone."*
What impression does this line give the reader of the Traveller as he leaves?

____

____

____

Compare and Contrast The Listeners

1. This poem focuses on the Traveller outside the house and the listeners inside the house. Write two ways the outside and inside are different.

____

____

____

____

2. *"To that voice from the world of men."*
Explain what the poet means by the world of men and how it differs from the other world described in the poem.

____

____

____

____

3. How does the character of the Traveller change throughout the poem?

____

____

____

____

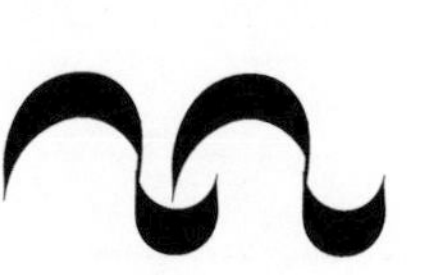

North of Time

by Rachel Field

We sat together in the small, square room,
Late sunshine fell across the kitchen floor
In yellow patches. I could hear the boom
Of turning tide along the island shore.
"Why, yes," the old man shifted in his chair,
"That's Grandfather's own chart hung by the door,
And that's his compass on the shelf up there.
He knew the world and foreign parts before
Most Island boys had learned their A.B.C.'s,
And how to cipher. He stood six feet two,–
It's queer to think a man like that should freeze
Sealing, up north in Greenland, but it's true,
And him not forty. Here I'm eighty odd
And not been south of Boston. Guess he'd say
Folks nowadays are like as peas in a pod,
And one port same's another all the way
Eastport to Hong Kong. He'd be right at that."
The kettle rocked with steam. The clock ticks told
The minutes off between us as we sat.
His eyes were age-filmed and his hands so old
They might have been dead roots. Dead roots? I thought
It can't be long before he's bound to go
After his Grandfather, to that same port
That's north of time, too far for charts to show
How currents run; what hidden reefs are near;
What headlands jut; what harbors to explore;
Or such a brass-bound compass serve to steer
The cruising souls along an unknown shore.

Vocabulary North of Time

1. *"He knew the world and foreign parts before"*

Which word is **not** another word for foreign?

	Tick **one**
distant	
domestic	
overseas	
remote	

2. Look at the first half of the poem.

Find and **copy one word** that is closest in meaning to doing arithmetic.

____

3. *"It's queer to think a man like that should freeze*
Sealing, up north in Greenland, but it's true,"

Explain what sealing means in this sentence.

____

4. **Find** and **copy a group of words** that means people in the present time.

____

5. **Find** and **copy two different phrases** that show the man was elderly.

1. ____

2. ____

Retrieval North of Time

1. a) What time of day was it when the narrator was speaking with the old man?

____

b) Where was the house located?

____

2. a) How did the old man's grandfather die?

____

b) How old was his grandfather when he died?

____

3. **Find** and **copy two** pieces of equipment his grandfather used on his adventures.

1. ____
2. ____

4. **Find** and **copy three** sounds the old man and the narrator could hear as they talked.

1. ____
2. ____
3. ____

5. Using information from the poem, put a tick in the correct box to show whether each statement is **true** or **false**.

	True	**False**
His grandfather sailed to Iceland.		
The old man is well travelled.		
The narrator doesn't think it will be long until the old man dies.		
The man's grandfather learned about travelling and adventure at a young age.		

Summary North of Time

1. What is the main message of the poem?

	Tick **one**
Death is life's final journey	
Death is dangerous	
Life is dangerous	
Family stays together	

2. Using information from the poem, tick one box in each row to show whether each summary statement is **true** or **false**.

	True	**False**
The old man's grandfather lived a life of adventure.		
The old man lived a life of adventure.		
The narrator thinks the old man will never see his grandfather again.		
Heaven is like another port on the journey.		

3. Is *North of Time* a good title for this poem? Give reasons for your answer.

	Tick **one**
yes	
no	

____

____

____

____

____

____

Inference North of Time

1. In the first half of the poem, **what evidence** is there that the old man's grandfather was an explorer?

2. Why is it *"queer to think a man like that should freeze"*? **Use evidence** from the poem to support your answer.

3. Where will the old man go to find his grandfather?

4. At the end of the poem (final five lines), what impression are we given of the way to the port north of time? **Use evidence** from the poem to support your answer.

5. Why is it that the port north of time is *"too far for charts to show"* and no one knows the way?

Prediction North of Time

1. After listening to the old man's stories of his life and of his grandfather, how do you think the narrator will choose to live her life?

Use evidence from the poem to support your prediction.

2. What will happen the next time the narrator goes to visit the old man?

Use evidence from the poem to support your prediction.

Text Meaning North of Time

1. Draw lines to match each poetic technique with the correct quotation from the poem.

alliteration	Folks nowadays are like as peas in a pod,
onomatopoeia	The clock ticks told
personification	I could hear the boom of the turning tide along the island shore.
simile	We sat together in the small, square room,

2. a) This poem has an alternate rhyme scheme.

Tick the rhyme scheme of the first four lines.

ABBA	
ABAC	
ABCD	
ABAB	

b) The rhythm of this poem is very consistent. How many beats are there in each line?

____

Author's Use of Language

North of Time

1. *"Folks nowadays are like as peas in a pod,"*

What does the simile as peas in a pod tell the reader about what the old man thinks his grandfather might say about people now?

	Tick **one**
Every person is different.	
Everyone likes to garden.	
People are the same now as they were back then.	
Everyone is similar. No one is unique.	

2. *"And one port same's another all the way Eastport to Hong Kong."*

What is the old man saying about the world?

3. **Find** and **copy one phrase** that is a **metaphor** for heaven.

4. *"They might have even been dead roots."*

What does this description suggest about the old man?

5. What impression does the phrase *"north of time"* give the reader?

6. Why is the **analogy** (extended metaphor) of sailing effective in describing death and going to heaven?

Compare and Contrast North of Time

1. How was the old man's grandfather different to the other boys he grew up with?

____

____

2. a) Give one way the old man and his grandfather are similar.

1. ____

b) Give two ways the old man and his grandfather are different.

1. ____
2. ____

3. **Find** and **copy four images** that help to compare death to going on a sailing journey.

1. ____
2. ____
3. ____
4. ____

The Tyger

by William Blake

Tyger, Tyger, burning bright,
In the forests of the night;
What immortal hand or eye,
Could frame thy fearful symmetry?

In what distant deeps or skies
Burnt the fire of thine eyes?
On what wings dare he aspire?
What the hand dare seize the fire?

And what shoulder, & what art,
Could twist the sinews of thy heart?
And when thy heart began to beat,
What dread hand? & what dread feet?

What the hammer? what the chain,
In what furnace was thy brain?
What the anvil? what dread grasp,
Dare its deadly terrors clasp!

When the stars threw down their spears
And water'd Heaven with their tears:
Did he smile his work to see?
Did he who made the Lamb make thee?

Tyger, Tyger, burning bright,
In the forests of the night:
What immortal hand or eye,
Dare frame thy fearful symmetry?

Vocabulary The Tyger

1. *"What immortal hand or eye,"*

The word immortal is referring to:

	Tick **one**
human	
animal	
godly	
physical	

2. Look at verse one.

Find and **copy one word** that is closest in meaning to **build**.

____

3. *"Could frame thy fearful symmetry?"*

Symmetry is a mathematical word to do with shape. What does it mean?

	Tick **one**
The shape is different on each side.	
The shape is covered in stripes.	
One half of the shape is the mirror image of the other half.	
The shape is orange and black.	

4. Look at verse two.

Find and **copy one word** that shows the maker of the Tyger was very ambitious when he dared to create such a fiery creature.

____

5. Look at verses three and four.

Find and **copy one word** that tells the reader that the one who created the Tyger must be someone to be feared as well. The same word is used in both verses.

____

Retrieval The Tyger

1. **Circle** the correct option to complete each sentence below:

a) The Tyger lives in

the grasslands	the jungle
the mountains	the forest

b) The Tyger's __________ were created in the distant deeps or skies.

wings	stripes
eyes	heart

c) The Tyger's brain was created in a __________ .

butcher's shop	blacksmith's workshop
carpenter's workshop	weaver's workshop

2. Name **four** tools used to create the Tyger's brain.

1. ______________________ 3. ______________________

2. ______________________ 4. ______________________

3. Using information from the text, put a tick in the correct box to show whether each statement is **true** or **false**.

	True	False
The poet wonders if the creator might have wings.		
The poet thinks the creator needed strength in his shoulder to create the Tyger's heart.		
The stars threw down their swords in defeat.		
The poet wonders if the creator also made the Lion.		

Summary The Tyger

1. Throughout this poem, the narrator asks many questions. **Number them 1–6** to show the order in which they appear in the text. The first one has been done for you.

Who could have the strength and skill to create the Tyger's heart?	
Did the same creator who made the Lamb also create the Tyger?	
Where were the Tyger's fiery eyes made?	
Who had the courage to dare to create the Tyger?	
What tools were used to create the Tyger's brain?	
Who could possibly have created such a fearsome creature?	**1**

2. Think about the whole poem. Which phrase best summarises what the poem is about?

	Tick **one**
Why does evil exist?	
The creation of nature requires skill, effort and artistry.	
The industrial revolution was difficult for many people.	
Good and evil exist together.	

Explain your choice with evidence from the text.

____

____

____

____

Inference The Tyger

1. Look at verse one.
What question is the poet asking about the Tyger?

____

____

2. Look at this line from the second verse:
"In what distant deeps or skies"
Which **two** places are being referred to as the distant deeps and the skies?

____

3. Look at verse three.
"And what shoulder, and what art,"
What does the poet mean by shoulder and art?
(What does the creator have to use to make the Tyger's heart?)

____

____

4. Some people say the stars in verse five represent angels who have done wrong and been sent out of heaven.
Write **two pieces** of **evidence** that show these *"stars"* have been defeated?
1. ____
2. ____

5. What impression is the reader given of the creator of the Tyger? **Use evidence** from the whole poem to support your answer.

____

____

____

____

____

Prediction The Tyger

1. In verse five, the narrator mentions *"the Lamb"*. Not only is this another name for Jesus, but it is also the name of another poem by William Blake that is a companion to *"The Tyger"*. What do you think the poem *"The Lamb"* is about? Explain your answer with reference to *"The Tyger"*.

2. Animals are often used as symbols of human characteristics. If you were to choose another animal to write a similar poem about, which animal would you choose and which human characteristics would it symbolise. Explain your choice.

Text Meaning The Tyger

1. a) Write words from the poem to complete the pairs of rhyming words.

aspire	
chain	
see	
eye	

b) What is unusual about the final rhyme of the poem? Why do you think this might be?

____

____

2. Draw lines to match each part of the poem with the correct poetic technique.

repetition	Tyger, Tyger, burning bright, In the forests of the night;
metaphor	What the hammer? what the chain, In what furnace was thy brain? What the anvil? what dread grasp,
rhyming couplet	Did he who made the Lamb make thee?
alliteration	Tyger, Tyger, burning bright,

Author's Use of Language The Tyger

1. *"Tyger, Tyger, burning bright,"*
What does the phrase burning bright suggest about the Tyger?

____

____

2. *"Could frame thy fearful symmetry?"*
What does the phrase fearful symmetry suggest about the Tyger?

____

____

3. *"Dare its deadly terrors clasp?"*
What does this line suggest about the Tyger?

____

____

4. **Find** and **copy three different words or phrases** from the poem that suggest the Tyger represents evil.

1. ____
2. ____
3. ____

5. Published in England in 1794, some people think The Tyger represents the industrial revolution in Britain and how difficult life was for the workers.

Find and **copy four different words or phrases** from the poem that help to build up a picture of industrialism, factories and technology.

1. ____
2. ____
3. ____
4. ____

Compare and Contrast The Tyger

1. In verse one, the poet describes the Tyger and the forest.
a) How are they different?

___

___

b) Why is this an effective description?

___

___

2. Write one way the Lamb and the Tyger might be similar.

___

___

3. a) The first and last verse are almost identical. What is different?

___

___

___

b) Why do you think the poet, William Blake, made this change?

___

___

___

A Musical Instrument

by Elizabeth Barrett Browning

I.

WHAT was he doing, the great god Pan,
   Down in the reeds by the river ?
Spreading ruin and scattering ban,
Splashing and paddling with hoofs of a goat,
And breaking the golden lilies afloat
   With the dragon-fly on the river.

II.

He tore out a reed, the great god Pan,
   From the deep cool bed of the river :
The limpid water turbidly ran,
And the broken lilies a-dying lay,
And the dragon-fly had fled away,
   Ere he brought it out of the river.

III.

High on the shore sate the great god Pan,
   While turbidly flowed the river;
And hacked and hewed as a great god can,
With his hard bleak steel at the patient reed,
Till there was not a sign of a leaf indeed
   To prove it fresh from the river.

IV.
He cut it short, did the great god Pan,
(How tall it stood in the river !)
Then drew the pith, like the heart of a man,
Steadily from the outside ring,
And notched the poor dry empty thing
In holes, as he sat by the river.

V.
This is the way,' laughed the great god Pan,
(Laughed while he sate by the river,)
"The only way, since gods began
To make sweet music, they could succeed."
Then, dropping his mouth to a hole in the reed,
He blew in power by the river.

VI.
Sweet, sweet, sweet, O Pan !
Piercing sweet by the river !
Blinding sweet, O great god Pan !
The sun on the hill forgot to die,
And the lilies revived, and the dragon-fly
Came back to dream on the river.

VII.
Yet half a beast is the great god Pan,
To laugh as he sits by the river,
Making a poet out of a man :
The true gods sigh for the cost and pain, —
For the reed which grows nevermore again
As a reed with the reeds in the river.

Vocabulary A Musical Instrument

1. *"Spreading ruin and scattering ban"*
What is Pan scattering around the river?

	Tick **one**
rubbish	
curses	
happiness	
gifts	

2. **Tick** the correct definition of the word **reed** in the second stanza.

	Tick **one**
To look at symbols or letters and make sense of them	
A wind instrument	
A part of a clarinet that the musician blows through	
Tall grass that grows in wet areas	

3. At the beginning of the poem, the water is described as **limpid,** then after Pan splashes through it, it is described as **turbid**.

What do you think each of these words mean?

limpid	
turbid	

4. In the second stanza, the word **Ere** is a conjunction telling us when the dragonfly flew away compared to when Pan brought the reed out of the river. Which is the correct meaning of **Ere**?

	Tick **one**
before	
after	
while	
as soon as	

Vocabulary A Musical Instrument

5. In the third stanza, **find** and **copy two verbs** that mean the same as cut.

____

6. *"Then drew the pith, like the heart of a man,"*
What do you think Pan is doing to the reed?

Drawing a picture of it	Stepping on it	Hollowing out the middle	Cutting it into pieces

7. *"...notched the poor dry empty thing"*
What does notched mean in this line?

Making v-shaped slits	Blowing into it	Cutting it in half	Breaking it

8. Look at stanza six. *"And the lilies revived..."*
Which is closest in meaning to revived?

	Tick **one**
awoke from sleep	
fell asleep	
regained consciousness	
died	

9. In the last stanza, **find** and **copy a group of words** that tells the reader that there is no way the reed will grow again.

____

____

____

Retrieval A Musical Instrument

1. The Greek god Pan is part man and part which other creature?

___

2. Which insect flew away and then returned once it was calm again?

___

3. Where did Pan sit with his reed?

___

4. What three things did Pan do to the reed?

1. ___
2. ___
3. ___

5. What happened to life near the river when Pan played the music?

___

6. Using information from the poem, put a tick in the correct box to show whether each statement is **true** or **false**.

	True	False
Pan was careful to protect the insects and plants in the river.		
Pan cut the reed with a knife.		
Pan made music by strumming the instrument.		
The true gods agreed with what Pan had done.		

A Musical Instrument

1. Which of the following could be another possible title for this poem?

	Tick **one**
A Peaceful Day by the River	
Kindness of the Gods	
Power over Nature	
The True God	

2. Below are some summaries of different stanzas of this poem. **Number them 1–7** to show the order in which they appear in the poem. The first one has been done for you.

Creating an instrument	
Is he a true god?	
Muddy death and decay	
The sweetest music	
Music's effect on nature	
Destruction in the river	1
Transformation of the reed	

Inference A Musical Instrument

1. Pan causes destruction and chaos in the river.
Find and **copy two pieces** of evidence from the first stanza that support this statement.

1. ______________________________

2. ______________________________

____

2. What impression is the reader given of Pan's character? Write **two statements** showing **evidence** to support each one.

____

____

____

____

3. What was it that Pan created from the reed? How do you know?

____

____

4. Look at the fifth stanza. How did Pan feel as he played music by the river? **Use evidence** from the poem to support your answer.

____

____

5. Look at the very end of the poem. What does the poet think of Pan's actions?

____

____

Prediction A Musical Instrument

1. What other mischief do you think Pan might get up to?
Make a reasonable prediction with reference to the poem.

____

____

____

____

____

____

Text Meaning A Musical Instrument

1. a) Which **two words** are repeated at the end of lines in every stanza?

____

____

b) Why has the poet done this?

____

____

2. What is the rhyme scheme of each stanza of this poem?

____

3. Write words from the poem to complete the rhyming pairs:

afloat	
indeed	
ring	
succeed	
die	
again	

Author's Use of Language

A Musical Instrument

1. *"And breaking the golden lilies afloat"*

What does this description suggest about nature and what Pan is doing to it?

____

____

2. Look at the second stanza.

Find and **copy four words or phrases** that suggest destruction.

1. ______________________
2. ______________________
3. ______________________
4. ______________________

3. *"Till there was not a sign of a leaf indeed*
To prove it fresh from the river"

What do these lines suggest about the reed after Pan had finished with it?

____

____

4. *"And notched the poor dry empty thing"*

How does the poet want the reader to feel about the reed?

____

5. Tick the correct figures of speech for each line from the poem.

	alliteration	**simile**	**personification**
Down in the reeds by the river			
The limpid water turbidly ran			
Then drew the pith, like the heart of a man,			
And hacked and hewed as a great god can			

Compare and Contrast

A Musical Instrument

1. How does the water in the river change as Pan splashes in it and tears out the reed at the beginning of the poem?

2. In the sixth stanza, the mood of the poem changes. How is the mood different at the end of the poem compared to the beginning?

3. a) Give **one** way Pan and the "*true gods*" are similar.

b) Give **one** way Pan and the "*true gods*" are different.

Answers

Night Clouds (pages 17–26)

Night Clouds – Vocabulary

1. porcelain
2. horses
3. pounding their (yellow) feet / running fast or hard
4. remote
5. Try your hardest!
6. vermillion

Night Clouds – Retrieval

1. rush (along the sky) / beating their golden hoofs / standing (on their hind legs) / pawing (at the green porcelain doors)
2. night
3. they will kick the stars and they will scatter across the sky
4. with one lick of its (vermillion) tongue
5.

	True	False
The sky is filled with stars.	x	
The door to the Heavens is open.		x
The poet thinks it will be easy for the mares to escape.		x
The tiger will destroy them with his paw.		x

Night Clouds – Summary

1. It is the only mention of clouds.
2. The night sky is compared to animals (mares and a tiger). They are moving across the sky, changing it as they go. The night turns into day with the arrival of the tiger showing that time and nature are always moving forwards and changing.

Night Clouds – Inference

1. mares – the clouds moving across the night sky
   tiger – the sun rising in the morning
2. They are rushing across the sky and pawing at the door as they try to get away from the tiger. The poet tells them to fly and strain their utmost.
3. They are trying to get away from the tiger.
4. fierce
5. He can do it with one lick of his tongue.
6. The poet prefers the mares because she is encouraging them to try to get away from the tiger. She says, "Fly, mares! Strain your utmost"

Night Clouds – Prediction

1. Any logical, thoughtful answer that refers to the text.
   The tiger will catch the mares and destroy them. The sun will rise and burn off the clouds leaving a clear sky.

Night Clouds – Text Meaning

1. alliteration – The white mares of the moon
   personification – rush along the sky

alliteration – Beating their golden hoofs upon the glass Heavens

description – the green porcelain doors

2. The shorter lines give a sense of urgency to the poem. The mares must move quickly to escape the tiger.

Night Clouds – Author's Use of Language

1. a) white / golden / Heavens

b. destroy / vermillion

2. sight

3. glass = It is clear, transparent / It is possible to see into heaven / It is shiny and smooth / It is reflecting the stars and moonlight / It lets the light through

   heavens = good / paradise / have lived a good life (know God)

4. It is full of stars / stars are everywhere like dust / It is possible to see the entire galaxy (Milky Way) / Apart from the few clouds, it is a clear night

5. The tiger is the sun rising and chasing away the night.

Night Clouds – Compare and Contrast

1. a) They are both moving across the sky. / They both symbolise something in the sky. / They are both animals.

b) The mare symbolises clouds while the tiger symbolises the sun / The mares are good (symbolise purity) however the tiger is bad (symbolises evil) / The mares are white but the tiger is red (vermillion). / The mares are delicate and magical but the tiger is fierce and a predator.

2. The mares gallop/run across the land just like clouds move across the sky in a breeze. / They move up and down and change shape as they stand on their hind legs like clouds do. / The mares are white and pure looking just like white clouds in the moonlight. / The mares seem magical and mysterious like clouds on a moonlit night.

3. Or

4. The night sky is white and golden in the moonlight however the day is full of the red of the sun. / There are clouds moving across the night sky but the day is taken over by the sun. / The night is full of stars while there is only the sun chasing away the clouds in the day.

An Autumn Evening (pages 27–35)

An Autumn Evening – Vocabulary

1. pennons
2. A dome is a rounded/curved top or lid that looks like half a ball. This suggests that the sunset is curving over the land below like a domed roof.
3. Cradling is a way of holding a baby. It's like the valleys are rocking the day to sleep.
4. runes – ancient writing or symbols

   mournful – full of sadness

5. The word gulf tells us it is a wide gap/space. It is clear so there are no clouds or anything else to block it. The unfathomed blue cannot be fully understood or, like the unfathomed depths of the sea, it cannot be measured – no one knows how far it goes.

An Autumn Evening – Retrieval

1. crocus, purple, crimson, silver, blue, gold
2. valleys, (boughs) trees, sky
3. (lone) winds, beckoning boughs, elfin voices
4. wander, look, listen, pause, drink
5. It is filled up (refreshed, full of happiness)

An Autumn Evening – Summary

1. Stop and take in the beauty of nature.

2. Any logical, thoughtful answer that refers to the text. It might include enjoying the beauty of the evening, pausing to make the most of nature and the beauty all around, the Autumn evening is magical and this moment will only exist for a short time so we should appreciate it, spending time in nature refreshes our souls/minds and makes us feel better.

An Autumn Evening – Inference

1. hushed (valleys), lone (winds)
2. silver, gold
3. elfin voices
4. The narrator is completely absorbed/engrossed in the beauty of the evening and incredibly happy.
5. She is stopping to enjoy her surroundings and take it all in. She doesn't want the moment to end.

An Autumn Evening – Prediction

1. Any logical, thoughtful answer that refers to the text.

The narrator must make the most of the beauty of nature and the autumn evening because winter is on its way. Soon there will be snow, rain, hail and cold. The wind will be bitter and people will not want to go out walking in the evening. Many of the plants will die. The trees will continue to lose their leaves (leafless trees, mournful melodies, lone winds blow, chilly purple air).

2. Any logical, thoughtful answer that mirrors some of the examples in the original first two verses.

eg, glowing, rose sky / clementine streaks / green, growing valleys / warm winds / trees full of buds / wild cherry blossom / warm scented air / magical fairy rings / elves amongst the spring flowers / new life

An Autumn Evening – Text Meaning

1. ABABCC
2.

sky	lie
trees	melodies
fir	stir
delight	night

3. action – And so I wander through the shadows
   personification – Scarfed with its crimson pennons
   alliteration – Above the darkening druid
   setting – Dark hills against a hollow crocus sky

An Autumn Evening – Author's Use of Language

1. harps, mournful melodies
2. A thin strand of silver moonlight is sewn or woven across the purple sky.
3. glimmers – it is sparkling, shining
   great – it is large
   gold – bright
4. harps, runes, mournful melodies, darkening druid glens, elfin voices, beckoning boughs, divine enchantment
5. beckoning boughs

6. Divine is godly and enchantment is magic. It is an other-worldly, magical moment. She is refreshed with power and magic that comes from something outside the normal world.

An Autumn Evening – Compare and Contrast

1. The hills are dark while/whereas the sky is colourful.
2. At night, the glen seems to come alive with magic – beckoning boughs and elfin voices.
3. Verse one and two are full of setting description while verse three is action / the narrator appears.

In Flanders Fields (pages 36–44)

In Flanders Fields – Vocabulary

1. a bird
2. scarce
3. fight
4. failing / die
5. break faith
6. will not be at peace

In Flanders Fields – Retrieval

1. between the crosses / in the graveyard or cemetery
2. In Flanders fields
3. The guns are too loud and drown out the sound of the larks singing.
4. They can't fight anymore (they have died) and need others to carry on the fight
5.

	True	False
The war continues on the ground	x	
The graves are marked with angels		x
The soldiers died weeks ago		x
The soldiers are at peace		x

In Flanders Fields – Summary

1. Any option is correct. Children receive a mark for being able to explain their choice using evidence from the text. Discussion of each option is key to helping children understand there are a number of themes to this poem.

In Flanders Fields – Inference

1. larks – nature / soldiers still fighting / life

guns – the on-going fight / the guns set off at a remembrance ceremony / death

2. There a number of possible answers: The men were full of life / They lived ordinary lives / They had family and friends who cared about them / They enjoyed the simple things in life / They sacrificed a lot to go to war.

3. They are passing on the torch like in a relay race. It's like a baton. They are not able to carry on any longer so they need others to continue on fighting for them.

It is a symbol of continuing to work for what is right and find peace.

4. Loved and were loved – Had friends and family at home

Now we lie – They have died

Saw sunset glow – Lived each day beginning to end

Short days ago – Death was sudden

5. Verse three

In Flanders Fields – Prediction

1. Any logical, thoughtful answer that refers to the text.

Sad – their friends have died (crosses, row on row / We are the Dead / now we lie, In Flanders fields)

Hopeful/Encouraged – others will carry on their fight (To you from failing hands we throw The torch; be yours to hold it high)

Nostalgic – remembering their life at home (lived, felt dawn, saw sunset glow, Loved and were loved)

In Flanders Fields – Text Meaning

1. The rhythm helps the reader to focus on keywords at the end of each line.
   The rhythm is similar to soldiers marching.
   The rhythm helps the reader to remember the poem.
2. rhyme: In Flanders fields the poppies blow
   Between the crosses row on row
   metaphor: To you from failing hands we throw
   The torch…
   repetition: In Flanders fields
   imagery: We lived, felt dawn, saw sunset glow

3.

blow	row
high	die
ago	glow
throw	foe

In Flanders Fields – Author's Use of Language

1. The soldiers who have died.
2. The repetition emphasises the great number of soldiers who died in battle.
3. The lark is described as brave just as the soldiers were.
4. The reader is being commanded (imperative verb – Take) to continue the fight the soldiers started and not let them down (break faith). The reader feels as if the soldiers are speaking directly to them and this makes the reader want to take action. It is our responsibility to remember and make sure this doesn't happen again. It is also our responsibility to pass the message on to others.
5. Any answer with clear reference to the text is acceptable.

It paints a clear picture of war.

It emphasises how many soldiers sacrificed their lives.

It is the beginning of the use of a poppy as a symbol of remembrance.

The rhythm makes it memorable.

It speaks directly to the reader.

In Flanders Fields – Compare and Contrast

1. The first line shows natural beauty and life but/whereas/however the second line shows the ugliness and devastation of war and death.

2. a) We are the Dead – life is over, they have sacrificed their lives, it is very final and feels cold

We lived, felt dawn, saw sunset glow / Loved and were loved – full of life and love, their days were full of good things, it feels warm

b) This shows the reader how much the soldiers sacrificed to fight in the war.

Leisure (pages 45–53)

Leisure – Vocabulary

1. branches
2. broad daylight / night
3. In the middle of the day when things can be easily seen
4. glimpse
5. enrich
6. stand and stare

Leisure – Retrieval

1. horses

2. stand and stare
3. sheep / cows
4. dancing / smile
5.

	True	False
The narrator doesn't have time to wait for happiness in the eyes to turn into a smile.	x	
The narrator feels life is very rich.		x
People often have to rush through the woods.	x	
The narrator looks at the stream at night.		x

Leisure – Summary

1. Yes – "Stop and smell the roses" means to take time to enjoy nature. The narrator of this poem is talking about how important it is to not rush through life and to enjoy simple things.

No – There isn't anything about roses in this poem so it wouldn't be the best title. Perhaps something about "Taking Time Through the Woods" or "Enjoy Nature" would be better.

2. It is important to work hard and keep busy.

Don't be lazy and waste time relaxing.

3. Yes, it is a timeless poem. In 1911, technology was advancing rapidly. Everyone was busier and working very hard. The same is true now. People get very busy with their work and distracted by technology so they don't have as much time to enjoy nature and take life at a slower pace.

Leisure – Inference

1. They are probably going to work or school. They are in a rush because they don't want to be late. They are distracted by everything they have to do. They are likely just walking through the woods because it is the quickest route.

2. Beauty might be the narrator's love or another woman he cares about (sister, mother, friend).

3. No time to stand under trees and look at nature.
   No time to enjoy the woods and watch the squirrels
   No time to look at the stream
   No time to stop and watch lovely dancing
   No time to look at someone's face and watch them smile.

4.

	Fact	Opinion
Everyone should stop and take time to enjoy nature.		x
People's lives are very busy with work and families.	x	
A smile is very beautiful.		x
Sheep and cows do not have the same responsibilities as people.	x	

5. He wishes life were different – Says this is a poor life

Life is richer when you take the time to enjoy nature – no time to stand and stare

Life is too busy – no time to stand and stare

Leisure – Prediction

1. Any logical, thoughtful answer that refers to the text, eg, He will try to work less and spend more time out in nature.
He might change his job so he's not so busy.
He will try to spend more time with the people he cares about.
He will make it a priority to notice what is going on around him as he walks through the woods.

2. Any logical, thoughtful answer that links to the text.

Leisure – Text Meaning

1. a). AABBCCDDEEFFGG
   b). Rhyming couplets

2.

care	stare
pass	grass
daylight	night
can	began

Leisure – Author's Use of Language

1. To emphasise the excuse people make for not taking time to enjoy nature and the world around them.
2. stand and stare / beneath the bows / streams full of stars
3. The sun is reflecting off the water so it is sparkling and twinkling like a starry sky at night.
4. Beauty dances and smiles. The beauty of the world is being compared to a woman.
5. It is a poor life because it does not have enough in it. It is the enjoyment of beauty and nature that makes life rich. People gain from stopping, relaxing and taking in the world around them.

Leisure – Compare and Contrast

1. Sheep and cows spend their day standing in fields and staring at the world around them. They don't seem to do much else.
2. They both twinkle and sparkle.
3. He hopes they will take more time to stand and stare (enjoy life and slow down). He hopes they will work less and be in less of a rush.

In the Bleak Midwinter (pages 54–62)

In the Bleak Midwinter – Vocabulary

1. dreary
2. support

3. sufficed
4. archangels / cherubim / seraphim
5. crowded together in the sky / filled the sky / packed in around him
6. I would do my part

In the Bleak Midwinter – Retrieval

1. winter
2. piles of snow
3. Heaven
4. Jesus
5. She is poor
6. a kiss
7. a lamb
8. her heart

In the Bleak Midwinter – Summary

1. Mother's Love/Nativity/Gifts
2.

Simple comforts were enough for him.	3
Angels gathered around as his mother loved him.	4
The world was cold and still.	1
Powerful Jesus came to earth.	2
Gifts for the baby.	5

In the Bleak Midwinter – Inference

1. midwinter / frosty wind / earth stood hard as iron / water like a stone / snow
2. He is so powerful that he can't be contained by Heaven or earth. / He is very powerful / He is too powerful for Heaven or earth.
3. Barn or stable – mangerful of hay / ox and ass and camel
   Enough for him – It repeats that is was enough for him
   Simple – it was a stable even though he was God
4. Came from Heaven / He comes to reign / The Lord God Almighty, Jesus Christ / cherubim worship / angels fall before him / Worshipped by his mother / What can I give Him?
5. She is the only one to touch or kiss him.

In the Bleak Midwinter – Prediction

1. Any logical, thoughtful answer that refers to the text.

eg, War was also bleak and cold. It was a Christmas song and they missed home at Christmas. It reminded them of home. They missed their mothers and others they loved. They felt like they needed God.

In the Bleak Midwinter – Text Meaning

1. AABB (CCDD / EEFF / GGHH / IIJJ)
2. It has clear, simple, straightforward rhymes and is musical.
3. The first four stanzas describe the scene. In the fifth stanza, the narrator speaks and links the scene to herself. She becomes a part of the poem.

In the Bleak Midwinter – Author's Use of Language

1. The w sound in midwinter, wind, water / The m sound in midwinter, made, moan
2. The long o sound in moan, stone, snow, ago
3. Earth stood hard as iron / water like a stone

4. personification
5. The angels are bowing down before the baby because he is a King (he came to reign)
6. She will give love / adoration to the baby.

In the Bleak Midwinter – Compare and Contrast

1. The description of the stable is simple and plain but/while/however Jesus is described as The Lord God Almighty so we might expect him to be born somewhere rich and elaborate like a palace.
2. She is the only one who touches or kisses the baby.
3. a) They all want to give the baby a gift.

   b) The shepherd and Wise Man bring physical gifts to the baby while/but/however the narrator gives her love (an abstract noun).

The shepherd and Wise Man know what to give as a gift but the narrator is not sure at first.

4. They both give love and adoration as their gift.

The Way Through the Woods (pages 63–72)

The Way Through the Woods – Vocabulary

1. Weather and rain have undone it again
2. coppice / heath
3. anemones
4. roll at ease
5. cantering
6. silence

The Way Through the Woods – Retrieval

1. 70 years
2. Planted trees
3. The keeper
4. They see so few of them
5. Beat of a horse's feet / swish of a skirt
6.

	True	False
You might see hedgehogs in the woods		x
Birds are raising their babies in the woods.	x	
The summer evenings are very warm.		x
It is very quiet in the woods at night.	x	

The Way Through the Woods – Summary

1. The power of nature.
2.

In the misty silence, no one is there and there is no road through the woods.	6
The animals are relaxed and unafraid.	4
On summer evenings, you might hear the sound of someone who once rode through the woods.	5
Only the keeper is able to visit the beauty of nature in the woods.	3
They manage the growth of the words by planting trees, cutting some back and letting other areas grow wild.	2
They shut the road through the woods.	1

The Way Through the Woods – Inference

1. Over 70 years old because he can remember the road through the woods and it closed 70 years ago.

2. Cares about nature – the only one who is able to visit the woods / manages the planting and coppicing of trees

Envied by the poet – the poet sees that the keeper is the only one who can visit the woods, beautiful in its nature and wishes he could too

Trusted by animals – the badgers roll at ease / the ring-dove has its babies

3. It is full of wonderful animals – ring-dove / badgers / trout / otter

It is quiet and peaceful – misty solitudes

It is cool and refreshing – When the night-air cools on the trout-ringed pools

4. They are no longer afraid of people because they see so few.

They are relaxed and confident because there is no traffic to disturb or frighten them.

They are thriving (growing and reproducing). They are having babies.

5. You will hear the beat of a horse's feet and the swish of a skirt in the dew.

It's like there is a ghostly presence or a memory of someone who used to ride on the road through the woods.

6.

	Fact	Opinion
The woods are better without the road.		x
The air is cooler in the evening.	x	
Otters and badgers live in the woods.	x	
There are ghosts in the woods.		x

The Way Through the Woods – Prediction

1. Any logical, thoughtful answer that refers to the text.

eg, Yes – There is so much beauty and wonderful plants and animals to see in the woods so everyone should be able to go there.

No – A road would destroy the nature in the woods. The animals would become frightened and plants would be destroyed.

2. Any logical, thoughtful answer that refers to the text.

eg, The animals will continue to be happy and have more babies. Their numbers will increase and the ecosystem will be healthy.

The Way Through the Woods – Text Meaning

1.

ago	know
late	mate
dew	few (through / knew)
trees	anemones (sees / ease)

2. Weather and rain have undone it again

It is underneath the coppice and heath

When the night-air cools on the trout-ringed pools

You will hear the beat of a horse's feet

The Way Through the Woods – Author's Use of Language

1. Weather and rain have undone it again

2. Curious because they want the reader to wonder what has happened to the road and why they shut it.

3. Cool and refreshing / peaceful and calm – the trout are not frightened and come to the surface of the pool

4. Happy (whistles) / confident (calls out to its mate) / healthy (mating)

5. The misty solitudes

The Way Through the Woods – Compare and Contrast

1. The road has disappeared. The trees, heath (heather/grasses) and flowers have grown over the road. The animals have become more confident. The woods are quiet and still.

When the road was still there, it would have been busy and noisy. The animals would have remained hidden. The trees and plants would have been cut back to make way for the road.

2. The animals used to be afraid and cautious around people but now they do not fear them because they see so few.

3. The beginning of the poem is calm and peaceful, focussing on nature. Towards the end, it changes to mystical and mysterious – The beat of a horse's feet and the swish of a skirt in the dew. There is the memory or a ghost of someone who used to ride through the woods.

"Hope" is the Thing with Feathers (pages 73–81)

"Hope" is the Thing with Feathers – Vocabulary

1. perches
2. severe
3. abash
4. harsh/difficult/hard
5. It expected very little in return

"Hope" is the Thing with Feathers – Retrieval

1. a) bird b) the soul

2.

	True	False
Hope sounds best in fierce winds.	x	
Hope stops singing when the person has enough.		x
Hope keeps people warm.	x	
Hope asks for payment.		x

3. chillest land / strangest Sea

"Hope" is the Thing with Feathers – Summary

1. Hope Eternal

2.

Hope survives in many difficult situations.	3
Hope's song is described	2
Hope asks for nothing in return.	4
The metaphor of Hope as a bird is introduced.	1

3. Wings or feathers / hope

"Hope" is the Thing with Feathers – Inference

1. a) the thing with feathers – a bird
   b) That could abash the little bird
2. feathers / perches / sings

3. the soul

4. Points – It is difficult / stormy / hard / cold / strange / hopeful

Evidence – in the Gale / the chillest land / the strangest Sea / in Extremity / hope perching in her soul even in difficult times

5. Warm / hopeful / more cheerful / like they can get through anything / like everything will be all right

"Hope" is the Thing with Feathers – Prediction

1. Any logical, thoughtful answer that refers to the text, eg, I might need the bird Hope if I was to move away to a new city and have to change schools. I would be sad and it might be difficult to make new friends. I would miss my old school, house and friends. Hope would help me to know that it will be OK and I will make new friends.

"Hope" is the Thing with Feathers – Text Meaning

1. Verse 1: ABCB
   Verse 2: ABAB
   Verse 3: ABBB
2. a) 8/6/8/6
   b) This rhythm is very musical and mimics the song of the bird, Hope.
3. First person – "I've" and "me" in the third verse.

"Hope" is the Thing with Feathers – Author's Use of Language

1. The song of Hope is universal and can be understood all over the world. It is not in only one language. It is for all people, in all times.
2. never stops – at all
3. That kept so many warm
4. alliteration – And sore must be the storm
   personification – That perches in the soul
   consonance – Hope is the thing with feathers (***th*** sound is repeated)
   alliteration – And on the strangest Sea
5. in the Gale / storm / chillest land / strangest Sea / Extremity

"Hope" is the Thing with Feathers – Compare and Contrast

1. Hope is being compared to a bird (thing with feathers)
2. Abstract nouns are feelings or ideas that cannot be seen or held. They are more difficult to understand. Comparing it to a concrete noun like a bird makes it easier to understand because we can see, hear and touch a bird.
3. The bird's song is sweet and warm while the narrator is in the middle of a strong storm and time of hardship.

The Highwayman (pages 82–96)

The Highwayman - Vocabulary

1. Ghostly suggests the moon is spooky / eerie / white / glowing.
   Galleon suggests it is like a large ship that sails / floats across the sky.
2. casement
3. waterfall
4. sniggering jest
5. twisted / writhed / stretched / strained
6. She strove no more for the rest.

The Highwayman – Retrieval

1. a) steal gold

b) standing very straight

c) at noon

d) on a winter's night

2. pistol / rapier

3. he is an ostler (looks after horses) / face was white and peaked / eyes were hollows of madness / hair like mouldy hay / loved Bess / he hid in the stable and listened to Bess and the Highwayman / he overheard the Highwayman's plan to steal gold

4. He was listening to Bess and the Highwayman talking. He overheard the Highwayman's plan to steal gold.

5. Drank (stole) the landlord's ale / gagged Bess / tied her up with a musket / kissed Bess

6. She pulled the trigger on the musket. The sound of the shot warned the Highwayman.

7. galleon / Highwayman / old inn-door / French cocked-hat / lace at his chin / breeches / pistol / rapier / cobbles / red-coat troop / King George's men / musket

8.

	True	False
The Highwayman knew Tim was listening		x
The Highwayman was on horseback	x	
The soldiers worked for King Edward		x
The soldiers stole money from the landlord		x

The Highwayman – Summary

1. True love lasts forever. Children may argue that other options are also messages of the poem. This question should prompt a good discussion.

2.

Soldiers came to the inn to wait for the Highwayman.	4
Tim listened from the stable.	2
The Highwayman promised to return with gold.	3
Bess killed herself to warn the Highwayman.	5
The Highwayman visited Bess at the inn.	1
The Highwayman returned to the inn to avenge Bess' death.	6

The Highwayman – Inference

1. He didn't want her father or anyone else to hear him or know he was there. Their relationship was probably a secret.

2. sneaky – (he is listening in the dark, hidden in the stable) "Dumb as a dog he listened"

weak / poorly / not fit or healthy – "his face was white and peaked"

dirty / doesn't care about his appearance or hygiene – "his hair like mouldy hay"

mentally ill / mad – "his eyes were hollows of madness"

loving – "he loved the landlord's daughter"

good with animals – an "ostler"

3. Her heart is pounding. She is very nervous / anxious / frightened for the Highwayman to return. "Her love's refrain" could be the repetitive "riding – riding – riding" meaning her heart is beating like a horse galloping.

4. Her eyes grew wide for a moment

5. She is very brave – she was willing to kill herself to protect her love

She is incredibly loving – she sacrificed her life for the Highwayman

6. shocked / upset – his face grew grey to hear it
   angry – spurred like a madman / shrieking a curse to the sky / rapier brandished high

The Highwayman – Prediction

1. Any logical, thoughtful answer that refers to the text.
2. Any logical, thoughtful answer that refers to the text.

The Highwayman – Text Meaning

1. repetition – riding – riding – riding
   onomatopoeia – *Tlot tlot*
   simile – Down like a dog on the highway
   metaphor – the road was a ribbon of moonlight
   symbolism – dark red love-knot

2. It shows three different sections of the poem. Part one is full of love and hope. It introduces the characters – Bess and the Highwayman are in love while Tim is listening in the stable. It also tells the reader the Highwayman's plan to go away and steal gold then return to Bess the next day.

Part two is full of darkness and death. It is about the soldiers coming for the Highwayman and Bess' death.

The epilogue repeats the opening verses and shows that even in death, love remains.

The Highwayman – Author's Use of Language

1. stormy – a torrent is something violent and fast flowing / the gusty trees
   dark – the wind brought darkness / there was only a ribbon (a small amount) of moonlight as the wind blew the clouds over the moon
   cloudy – the moon came in and out of the clouds as the wind blew the clouds across the sky
2. hair like mouldy hay / dumb as a dog
3. Hell represents the soldiers catching him, being arrested, being killed, death. The Highwayman means he will overcome any obstacle to return to Bess (like the saying "Come hell or high water")
4. It seemed to take ages / a very long time for the Highwayman to return. Because she was so anxious and frightened, it made it seem even longer.
5. The sound of the gunshot exploded in the quiet of the night. All the peace of the night was broken by the loud sound. It also shattered the life they had before. It could never be the same again.

The gunshot also represents Bess' sacrifice to save her love.

6. Their love is strong like a knot. It is long-lasting like the length of her hair. Their lives are forever entwined like the plait. The red of the ribbon represents love (but could also symbolise death).
7. a) love / death (blood)
   b) coat of claret velvet / a dark red love-knot / landlord's red-lipped daughter / tawny sunset / red-coat troop / Blood red were his spurs / wine-red was his velvet coat

The Highwayman – Compare and Contrast

1. The Highwayman – twinkle / The inn-yard – dark
2. Bess is beautiful (dark-eyed, red-lipped, long dark hair) whereas/while/however Tim looks pale and unhealthy (face was white and peaked, hair like mouldy hay).

Tim remains hidden in the stable but/however Bess comes to the window to see the Highwayman.

Bess shares love with the Highwayman while Tim loves but is not loved in return.

3. Similar – They will still meet at Bess's window on winter's nights. She will let her hair down so he can kiss it. They will relive that night over and over again. They will always have their love for each other.

Difference – They will never be able to have any other experiences together. Their lives will never move forward.

The Listeners (pages 97–108)

The Listeners – Vocabulary

1. smote
2. confused
3. host / thronging
4. hearkening
5. Eating the grass
6. The silence returned to the house as the man galloped away on his horse. The silence came quickly with force (like a wave).

The Listeners – Retrieval

1.  A house with one turret.
2. In the forest / one turret / high window / very quiet / staircase inside / empty hall
3. phantoms / ghosts
4. 3
5. He had made a promise to someone in the house.

The Listeners – Summary

1. Yes or no with an explanation to justify the answer. Reference to the Traveller's knocks and calls remaining unanswered.

2.

The Traveller knocked on the door but no one came.	2
The phantoms heard the Traveller leave.	6
The Traveller knocked on the door as a bird flew away.	1
No one looked out the window at the Traveller.	3
The Listeners gathered on the stair.	4
The Traveller cried out that he had kept his word to come.	5

The Listeners – Inference

1. He is on a journey / It is not his house / He has come from far away
2. forest's ferny floor / bird flew out of the turret / leaf-fringed sill
3. night – moonlit door / quiet of the moonlight / faint moonbeams / starred and leafy sky
4. (To that voice from) the world of men
5. And he felt in his heart their strangeness
6. He wants to see or speak to someone ("Is there anybody there?"). He gave someone his word that he would come ("Tell them I came, and no one answered, That I kept my word").

He's quite desperate for someone to answer the door. He becomes more agitated each time he knocks. He knocks quite forcefully ("And he smote on the door again a second time").

7. The listeners can hear him but are only able to / willing to respond with silence. Even though he is crying out, they won't answer. They don't seem to be sympathetic or concerned.

The Listeners – Prediction

1. Any logical, thoughtful answer that refers to the text.
2. Any logical, thoughtful answer that refers to the text.

The Listeners – Text Meaning

1. alliteration – Of the forest's ferny floor:
   onomatopoeia – And his horse in the silence champed the grasses
   personification – The stillness answering his cry,
   imagery – Hearkening in an air stirred and shaken

The Listeners – Author's Use of Language

1. moonlit / silence / phantom / lone / quiet / dark / empty / stirred / shaken / lonely / stillness / cry / echoing / shadowiness

2. Nature is taking over the house and covering it with plants. / No one has been in the house for a long time – it has become overgrown.

3. "Grey eyes" suggest the Traveller is lonely, lost, sad. It is a stormy colour suggesting anger or unhappiness. Grey is quiet which mimics the silence of the house.

4. silence / but no one descended / still / in the lone house / stood listening in the quiet of the moonlight / empty hall / no one answered / never the least stir / silence surged softly backward

5. The Traveller's call shatters / breaks the silence. It is so quiet that his call is a shock / a big contrast. The noise of his knocking and call destroys the silence of the house.

6. forest's ferny floor / Leaned over and looked / stood perplexed and still / stirred and shaken / suddenly smote / Louder, and lifted / silence surged softly

7. The repetition of the "f" and "s" sounds makes a sound a bit like shhh or the wind. It adds to the theme of silence.

8. The Traveller is becoming frustrated that no one is answering his call. Smote tells the reader that he bangs loudly on the door. His call becomes louder each time he knocks. He is desperate for someone to answer him.

9. It is repeated in echoes throughout the house – into every shadowy corner. The house is so quiet that his call fills the space.

10. Plunging hoofs shows that the Traveller gallops away quickly. Plunging is a forceful word. Then the sound dies away and the silence takes over again.

The Listeners – Compare and Contrast

1. Outside the house, there is life (the Traveller, the bird, the forest, the horse) but/while/however inside the house there is no life – only ghosts.

   Outside the house there is noise (the knocking and calling of the Traveller) but/while/however inside the house it is silent and still.

   Outside the house there is moonlight but/while/however inside the house it is dark and shadowy.

2. The Traveller is the only one alive ("the one man left awake") and from the world of men. The world of men is noisy with calling, crying and knocking. The other world is the world of phantoms or ghosts and is silent. They just listen.

3. As the poem progresses, the Traveller becomes more agitated / desperate for someone to answer his call. His knock and call become louder and he lifts his head to try to make himself heard.

North of Time (pages 109–117)

North of Time – Vocabulary

1. domestic
2. ciphers
3. Hunting for seals (in the Arctic)
4. Folks nowadays
5. the old man or his hands so old / I'm eighty odd / eyes were filmed with age

North of Time – Retrieval

1. a) late afternoon / late in the day
   b) on an island / near the shore / near the sea
2. a) He froze (when out sealing / on a trip to Greenland)
   b) Not (yet) forty
3. chart / compass
4. boom of the turning tide (waves) / kettle steaming / clock ticking
5.

	True	False
His grandfather sailed to Iceland.		x
The old man is well travelled.		x
The narrator doesn't think it will be long until the old man dies.	x	
The man's grandfather learned about travelling and adventure at a young age.	x	

North of Time – Summary

1. Death is life's final journey.
2.

	True	False
The old man's grandfather lived a life of adventure.	x	
The old man lived a life of adventure.		x
The narrator thinks the old man will never see his grandfather again.		x
Heaven is like another port on the journey.	x	

3. Any logical, thoughtful answer that refers to the text.

North of Time – Inference

1. chart / compass / he knew the world / he went to foreign parts / he was sealing up north in Greenland
2. He was big and strong – "He stood six feet two,"
   He had the right equipment – "That's Grandfather's own chart… and that's his com -pass"
   He had knowledge of the world – "He knew the world and foreign parts…"
   He had experience – "He knew the world and foreign parts before most island boys had learned their ABC's"
3. He will go to a port north of time which is a metaphor for heaven / the afterlife.
4. Unknown – "too far for charts to show how currents run" / "unknown shore"

Dangerous – "what hidden reefs are near; what headlands jut"

New places to explore – "What harbours to explore"

We don't know how to get there – how "such a brass-bound compass serves to steer the cruising souls to an unknown shore."

5. No one ever comes back to tell others how to get there. The only people who have gone there have died.

North of Time – Prediction

1. Any logical, thoughtful answer that refers to the text.
eg, She will be inspired by the man's grandfather and live a life of adventure. She might travel the world and learn about foreign parts.
eg, She might be like the old man and stay close to home where it is safe.

2. Any logical, thoughtful answer that refers to the text.

eg, The old man might have died and gone to be with his grandfather in heaven / the port north of time. She might go to his funeral.

eg, They might talk more about his grandfather and the adventures he had. The narrator might want to know more about his equipment or why he was sealing in Greenland.

North of Time – Text Meaning

1. alliteration – We sat together in the small, square room,

   onomatopoeia – I could hear the boom of the turning tide along the island shore.

   personification – The clock ticks told

   simile – Folks nowadays are like as peas in a pod,

2. a) ABAB

   b) 10

North of Time – Author's Use of Language

1. Everyone is similar. No one is unique.

2. Places across the world are more similar now than they used to be. You could find the same things in Eastport (northern Maine, USA and Hong Kong). It is not as exciting or different to travel to different ports now. Technology, communication and travel have made knowing about other places in the world much easier.

3. that same port that's north of time

4. dead – he is old / withered / his body is no longer getting what it needs / he is running out of energy (life)

roots – he is grounded / not going anywhere / he has not travelled far

5. This question should prompt some good discussion about the concepts of time and death.

North – far away, beyond everything else, above, past, north is often associated with cold

Time – life is marked by time; it controls everything we do. Once we are dead, time stops for us. Live on forever in Heaven / eternity.

6. The end of life is described as an unknown journey. There are no charts or maps to show us the way but we still find our way to heaven/after life/death. It helps the reader to imagine souls journeying to their final port/destination. Could the brass-bound compass be God or whoever is steering people the right way?

North of Time – Compare and Contrast

1. He knew the world and foreign parts at a very young age before the other boys had even been to school or started learning their ABCs and numbers (ciphers).

2. a) They both lived on the island / in the same house

   b) Grandfather was not even forty when he died but the old man had lived to over eighty.

   Grandfather had travelled all over the world on the other hand/while the old man had not been south of Boston (he had not travelled very much).

3. that same port / too far for charts to show / how currents run / what hidden reefs are near / what headlands jut / what harbors to explore / a brass-bound compass serve to steer / cruising souls / unknown shore

The Tyger (pages 118–126)

The Tyger – Vocabulary

1. godly
2. frame
3. One half of the shape is the mirror image of the other half.
4. aspire
5. dread

The Tyger – Retrieval

1. a) the forest
   b) eyes
   c) blacksmith's workshop
2. hammer / chain / furnace / anvil
3.

	True	False
The poet wonders if the creator might have wings.	x	
The poet thinks the creator needed strength in his shoulder to create the Tyger's heart.	x	
The stars threw down their swords in defeat.		x
The poet wonders if the creator also made the Lion.		x

The Tyger – Summary

1.

Who could have the strength and skill to create the Tyger's heart?	3
Did the same creator who made the Lamb also create the Tyger?	5
Where were the Tyger's fiery eyes made?	2
Who had the courage to dare to create the Tyger?	6
What tools were used to create the Tyger's brain?	4
Who could possibly have created such a fearsome creature?	1

2. Any option is correct. Children receive a mark for being able to explain their choice using evidence from the text. Discussion of each option is key to help children understand there are a number of themes to this poem.

The Tyger – Inference

1. Who created such a fearsome creature? / Who created the Tyger?
2. hell and heaven (the clue is in the mention of "immortal")
3. shoulder – hard work / effort / strength
   art – talent / skill / creativity
4. They threw down their spears (weapons). / They cried (water's heaven with their tears).
5. a god / live forever – "immortal"
   living in hell or heaven – "In what distant deep or skies"
   ambitious / trying something difficult – "dare he aspire"
   brave / confident – "dare seize the fire" / "Dare frame thy fearful symmetry"
   strong / hard-working – "And what shoulder"
   creative / talented / artistic – "& what art"
   fearsome / dangerous – "What dread hand? and what dread feet?"

Christian God – defeated "the stars" which are bad angels and created "the Lamb" which represents Jesus.

The Tyger – Prediction

1. Any logical prediction linked to The Tyger.

The Lamb is actually about who made the lamb with a series of statements about all of its positive, gentle, soft qualities. The poet tells the lamb that it has been created by someone who is also called the Lamb (Jesus / God).

2. Any logical, thoughtful answer that links to the text. For example, a poem about an eagle could symbolise freedom and power because an eagle can fly anywhere and is a great hunter.

The Tyger – Text Meaning

1. a)

aspire	fire
chain	brain
see	thee
eye	symmetry

b) Eye and symmetry don't really rhyme. There are two reasons why William Blake might have used this pair of words. First, it may be that he pronounced symmetry to rhyme with eye. In the past (around the time of Shakespeare) some words ending in '**y**' were pronounced with a long '*i*' sound at the end rather than a long '***e***' sound. Blake may have just preferred this pronunciation and felt it worked for his poem. The second reason may be that William Blake meant to write an awkward rhyme to contrast to the symmetry of the Tyger or for impact.

2. repetition — What the hammer? what the chain,
In what furnace was thy brain?
What the anvil? what dread grasp,

metaphor — Did he who made the Lamb make thee?

rhyming couplet — Tyger Tyger, burning bright,
In the forests of the night;

alliteration — Tyger Tyger, burning bright,

The Tyger – Author's Use of Language

1. It is brightly coloured. / It has a fire inside of it – this could be evil, fierceness or determination.
2. fearful – it should be feared / it is scary

   symmetry – it has markings/stripes/a pattern that is the same on both sides / symmetry was considered very beautiful
3. dare – it is risky to create a Tyger

   deadly terrors – the Tyger is frightening, evil, killing

   clasp – the creator has to hold onto the Tyger tightly
4. burning / fearful / distant deeps / burnt the fire / seize the fire / deadly terrors
5. frame / symmetry / seize the fire / what shoulder / what art / twist the sinews of thy heart / hammer / chain / furnace / anvil

The Tyger – Compare and Contrast

1. a) The Tyger is brightly coloured but/whereas/however the forest is dark (of the night).

   b) The Tyger stands out against the darkness.
2. They were created by the same god. / They both symbolise something.

3. a) The final line of the first verse begins with "Could" but in the last verse, the final line begins with "Dare".

   b) The first verse is asking who is skilled enough / able to create the Tyger but the last verse is asking who is brave enough to dare to create such a fearsome creature. They might be able to but will they actually dare to do it?

A Musical Instrument (pages 127–137)

A Musical Instrument – Vocabulary

1. curses
2. Tall grass that grows in wet areas
3. limpid = clear / transparent
   turbid = muddy / murky / opaque
4. before
5. hacked / hewed
6. hollowing out the middle (compared to removing the heart of a man)
7. making v-shaped slits
8. regained consciousness
9. For the reed which grows nevermore again

A Musical Instrument – Retrieval

1. goat
2. dragon-fly
3. High on the shore
4. cut it short / drew the pith (hollowed it out) / notched it
5. It went back to the peaceful state it was in before he disturbed it.
6.

	True	False
Pan was careful to protect the insects and plants in the river.		x
Pan cut the reed with a knife.	x	
Pan made music by strumming the instrument.		x
The true gods agreed with what Pan had done.		x

A Musical Instrument – Summary

1. Power over Nature
2.

Creating an instrument	4
Is he a true god?	7
Muddy death and decay	2
The sweetest music	5
Music's effect on nature	6
Destruction in the river	1
Transformation of the reed	3

A Musical Instrument – Inference

1. spreading ruin / scattering ban / breaking the golden lilies

2. destructive – spreading ruin / scattering ban / breaking the golden lilies / tore out a reed/ hacked and hewed

   wants to be powerful – high on the shore / tore out a reed (just takes what he wants) / laughed as he did it

   animal-like – hoofs of a goat / half a beast

   violent – hacked and hewed / hard bleak steel / drew the pith, like the heart of a man

3. a flute – hollow, notched, blew in it

4. happy / joyful – he laughed and played music

5. The poet thinks Pan was wrong to destroy nature and is not a true god. She refers to him as half a beast. He is cruel in how he laughs at what he has done.

A Musical Instrument – Prediction

1. Any logical, thoughtful prediction that refers to the poem and the qualities of Pan, eg, Destroying another part of nature to make something for himself.

A Musical Instrument – Text Meaning

1. a) Pan / river

   b) To make it clear that Pan is the central character. To emphasise the difference between Pan and the river (nature).

2. ABACCB

3.

afloat	goat
indeed	reed
ring	thing
succeed	reed
die	dragon-fly
again	pain

A Musical Instrument – Author's Use of Language

1. The golden lilies are beautiful and delicate. Pan is destroying nature.
2. tore / turbidly / broken / dying / fled
3. There is nothing left to identify it as a reed from the river. Pan has completely changed it.
4. The poet wants the reader to feel sorry for the reed and nature.
5. alliteration — Down in the reeds by the river

   personification — The limpid water turbidly ran

   simile — Then drew the pith, like the heart of a man

   alliteration / simile — And hacked and hewed as a great god can.

A Musical Instrument – Compare and Contrast

1. It changes from clear/transparent (limpid) to muddy and murky (turbid).

2. In the sixth stanza, the poem becomes peaceful and calm once more. The lilies are revived and the dragon-fly returns. At the beginning of the poem, it is full of destruction and chaos.

3. a) They both have power over nature.

   b) Pan chooses to hurt and destroy nature but true gods would not cause cost and pain.

References

English Reading Test Framework, National Curriculum Tests from 2016, 2016 Key Stage 2 English Reading Test Framework: National Curriculum Tests from 2016 Electronic version product code: STA/15/7341/e ISBN: 978-1-78315-826-3

Lexico. Definition of classic in English. https://www.lexico.com/en/definition/classic

The National Curriculum in England Framework *document* December 2014, Reference: DFE-00177-2013

Barrett Browning, Elizabeth. "A Musical Instrument". Poems Before Congress. London: Chapman & Hall, 1860.

Barrett Browning, Elizabeth. "A Musical Instrument". The Collected Poems of Elizabeth Barrett Browning. Ware, Hertfordshire: Wordsworth Editions Ltd, 2015.

Blake, William. "The Tyger". Songs of Experience. 1794.

Blake, William. "The Tyger". The Nation's Favourite Poems. BBC Worldwide Ltd, 1996.

Davies, W.H. "Leisure". Songs of Joy and Others. University of California Libraries, 1911.

Davies, W.H. "Leisure". The Nation's Favourite Poems. BBC Worldwide Ltd, 1996.

De la Mare, Walter. The Listeners. London: Constable and Company, 1912.

De la Mare, Walter. "The Listeners". The Nation's Favourite Poems. BBC Worldwide Ltd, 1996.

Dickinson, Emily. "Hope is the Thing with Feathers". Poems by Emily Dickinson, second series. Boston: Roberts Brothers, 1891

Dickinson, Emily. "Hope is the Thing with Feathers". Emily Dickinson: Complete Poems. Arthur Wallens, 2019.

Field, Rachel. "North of Time". Fear is the Thorn. New York : Macmillan Co., 1936. https://www.poemhunter.com/poem/north-of-time/

Kipling, Rudyard. "The Way Through the Woods". Rewards and fairies: Historical Fantasy. London: Macmillan & Co., Limited, 1910.

Kipling, Rudyard. "The Way Through the Woods". The Nation's Favourite Poems. BBC Worldwide Ltd, 1996.

Lowell, Amy. "Night Clouds". What's O'Clock. Boston: Houghton Mifflin, 1925.

Lowell, Amy. "Night Clouds". The Kingfisher Book of Children's Poetry. London: Kingfisher Books Ltd, 1985.

McCrae, John. "In Flanders Fields". Punch Magazine, December 1915.

McCrae, John. "In Flanders Fields". In Flanders Fields and Other Poems. Project Gutenberg, 2008.

Montgomery, L.M. "An Autumn Evening". The Watchman and Other Poems. Toronto: McClelland, Goodchild & Stewart, Limited, 1906.

Montgomery, L.M. "An Autumn Evening". Ultimate Collection. e-artnow, 2016.

Noyes, Alfred. "The Highwayman". Blackwood's Magazine, August 1906.
Noyes, Alfred. "The Highwayman". The Nation's Favourite Poems. BBC Worldwide Ltd, 1996.

Rossetti, Christina. "In the Bleak Midwinter" (A Christmas Carol) Scribner's Monthly. January 1872.

Information about Poets & Poems:

All Poetry. Rachel Lyman Field. (accessed February 2020) https://allpoetry.com/Rachel-Lyman-Field

Asda, Omer. The Tyger by William Blake. Poem Analysis. (accessed January 2020) https://poemanalysis.com/william-blake/the-Tyger/

Baldwin, Emma. A Musical Instrument by Elizabeth Barrett Browning. Poem Analysis. (accessed April 2020) https://poemanalysis.com/elizabeth-barrett-browning/a-musical-instrument/

Baldwin, Emma. Analysis and Theme of The Way through the Woods by Rudyard Kipling. Beaming Notes. 2014. (accessed May 2020) https://beamingnotes.com/2014/09/25/analysis-theme-way-woods-rudyard-kipling/

Baldwin, Emma. In the Bleak Midwinter by Christina Rossetti. (accessed April 2020) https://poemanalysis.com/christina-rossetti/in-the-bleak-midwinter

Baldwin, Emma. The Listeners by Walter de la Mare. Poem Analysis. (accessed January 2020) https://poemanalysis.com/walter-de-la-mare/the-listeners/

Baldwin, Emma. The Way Through the Woods by Rudyard Kipling. Poem Analysis. (accessed May 2020) https://poemanalysis.com/rudyard-kipling/the-way-through-the-woods/

Bradshaw, Melissa. Amy Lowell. Oxford Bibliographies, 2014 (accessed: May 2020) https://www.oxfordbibliographies.com/view/document/obo-9780199827251/obo-9780199827251-0143.xml

Howard, James. The Tyger Summary & Analysis. Lit Charts. (accessed January 2020) https://www.litcharts.com/poetry/william-blake/the-Tyger

Johnson Lewis, Jone. Amy Lowell: American Poet and Imaginist. Thought Co., 2017. (accessed: May 2020) https://www.thoughtco.com/amy-lowell-biography-3530884

Literary Devices. In the Bleak Midwinter. (accessed April 2020) https://literarydevices.net/in-the-bleak-midwinter/

O'Brien, Liam. The Listeners Summary & Analysis. Lit Charts. (accessed January 2020) https://www.litcharts.com/poetry/walter-de-la-mare/the-listeners

Poetry Foundation. Rachel Field. (accessed February 2020) https://www.poetryfoundation.org/poets/rachel-field

Siri Andrews (ed.) The Hewins Lectures 1947-1962. Boston: The Horn Book, Incorporated, 1963. p.17.

Spacey, Andrew. Analysis of Poem Hope Is The Thing With Feathers by Emily Dickinson. Owlcation. (accessed April 2020) https://owlcation.com/humanities/Analysis-of-Poem-Hope-Is-The-Thing-With-Feathers-by-Emily-Dickinson

Spark Notes. Dickinson's Poetry. (accessed April 2020) https://www.sparknotes.com/poetry/dickinson/section2/

Acknowledgements

"The Listeners" by Walter de la Mare from Collected Poems, Faber & Faber, 1979. Reproduced by permission of The Literary Trustees of Walter de la Mare and The Society of Authors as their Representative

"The Highwayman" by Alfred Noyes. Reproduced by permission of The Society of Authors as the Literary Representatives of the Estate of Alfred Noyes

Every effort has been made to trace copyright holders and to obtain their permission for the use of copyright material. In some instance we have been unable to trace the owners of copyright material and we would appreciate any information that would enable us to do so. The publisher will put right any errors or omissions in the list in future reprints or editions of this book.

Photograph/Illustration Credits

Every effort has been made to trace copyright holders and to obtain their permission for the use of copyright material. The publisher apologises for any errors or omissions in the list and would be grateful for notification of any corrections that should be incorporated in future reprints or editions of this book.

Night clouds; Absfreepic.com
Cumulus: Harmony Center: Pixabay
Sunrise; S. Hermann & F. Richter: Pixabay
Tree; J. Plenio: Pixabay
Poppy; Couleur: Pixabay
In remembrance WW1; Absfreepic.com
Crowd of people; Absfreepic.com
Reed; Rudy and Peter Skitterians: Pixabay
Ballet shoes; Lynnea: Pixabay
Horses: Walterri Paulatiarju: Pixabay
Sheep; Sara Price: Pixabay
Roses; Reenablack: Pixabay
Night Sky with Man: Absfreepic
Sheep; Sara Price: Pixabay
Christmas; Gerd Altmann: Pixabay
Nativity in Manger by Gaynor Berry
Virgin Mary; Gordon Johnson: Pixabay
Otters; Gerhard C: Pixabay
Dove; Dmitry Biryukov: Pixabay
Bird; Homercar 119: Pixaby
Villa; Peter H: Pixabay
House; Steve Brandon: Pixabay
Spirit; Darkmoon Art: Pixabay
Lighthouse; Wolfgang Claussen: Pixabay
Old farmhouse; Myriam Zilles: Pixabay
Castle; Shutterbug 75: Pixabay
Map of the World; Shaeffler: Pixabay
Pond; Mabel Amber: Pixabay
"Sweet, piercing sweet was the music of Pan's pipe" reads the caption on this depiction of Pan (by Walter Crane): Wikipedia